SPACEPOWER

what it means to you

Plate 1—High Altitude Research Vehicles

Three typical UN Space Force vehicles in flight. The two
lower vehicles are shown re-entering the earth's atmosphere.

SPACEPOWER
what it means to you

by Donald Cox and Michael Stoiko
illustrated by N. Stanilla

THE JOHN C. WINSTON COMPANY
Philadelphia · Toronto

To Jane Dallas and Donalee

(our daughters)

. . . future citizens of a space world . . .

Where there is no vision, the people perish.

—Prov. 29:18

about the authors

THOUGH both authors are directly concerned with missile projects in the United States, it was a desire to broaden their personal knowledge of other aspects of air penetration that led to the writing of this book. Michael Stoiko, an aviation engineer, has worked for the last twenty-one years on various phases of space flight. Even though his occupation has been wholly centered on the pure mechanics of space flight, he realized that technical knowledge was not the all-encompassing solution to the problems engendered by advancements in that field. Donald Cox, on the other hand, because his participation has been of a less technical nature, felt the need for a deeper comprehension of the mechanics of the exploration of space. Their interests met; the result was SPACEPOWER.

DONALD Cox was born in Rutherford, New Jersey, in the third decade of this century. He attended high school there, and, later, was graduated with a bachelor of arts degree from nearby Montclair State Teachers College. After a two-year stint in the United States Army Air Force in China, Burma, and India as a weather observer and forecaster, he returned to this country to resume his schooling. He matriculated at Columbia University, and, in 1948, received his doctorate in education. He then taught for nine years at the Air Command and Staff College in Montgomery, Alabama, and at the universities of Florida and Alabama. He left the teaching field in 1957 to assume his present position as the head of an information service for one of this country's largest aircraft manufacturers.

MICHAEL STOIKO is a native of New York City. He was born and received his early schooling in that city. His training in aviation has been a combination of practice and theory, beginning as long ago as 1937 when, as a young man, he swept hangars and did aircraft mechanics work at the old Floyd Bennett Airport in New York.

During World War II, Mr. Stoiko served five years with the Marines in the Pacific Theater. His earlier practical experience in aircraft mechanics was made use of: he helped keep planes flying with the aid of whatever materials were at hand. After the war he completed his academic training in aeronautical engineering at the Polytechnic Institute of Brooklyn. He then went to the General Electric Company in Schenectady, New York, and worked on the A-3 Project Hermes missile. He is no longer with the General Electric Company, but since that time has worked solely on missile projects.

Mr. Stoiko has authored many technical articles which have appeared in aviation magazines. He is a member of the American Rocket Society and a Fellow of the British Interplanetary Society.

about the illustrator

N. STANILLA, though originally a Pennsylvanian, now lives near his work in Baltimore, Maryland.

His experience has been varied, as suits the artistic bent. He has traveled widely throughout the United States, and as high above it as private flying and long hours at astronomical telescopes will allow him.

Mr. Stanilla was schooled in New Castle, Pennsylvania, and Baltimore, Maryland, and served five years in the armed services.

His illustrations, as the reader can easily see, fully depict the schematic necessities of technical drawing, and, at the same time, retain the esthetic qualities that are essential to fine art.

contents

list of illustrations

preface

After running the motor a few minutes to heat it up, I released the wire that held the machine to the track and the machine started forward. Wilbur ran at the side, holding the wing to balance it. . . . The machine started (up) very slowly. . . . The flight lasted only 12 seconds but it was nevertheless the first in the history of the world in which a machine carrying a man had raised itself by its own power into the air.

Orville Wright—1903
The New York Times—October 6, 1957

ADVANCES in the social and physical sciences, as in other fields, are usually brought about by a slow process of evolution—by the cumulative effects of innumerable small contributions.

The history of modern technology, particularly rocketry, has been the story of such a process.

Recently, however, four historic events have occurred which, considered in themselves, are milestones in the history of modern technological development. But when these seemingly independent occurrences are considered together—related to rocketry—they have a phenomenal catalytic effect on this normally slow process.

The first such event occurred on the evening of September 8, 1944, the date the first German vengeance weapon, the V-2, fell on London. The second event, which startled the world on the morning of August 6, 1945, was the nuclear destruction of Hiroshima. The third event occurred just before noon on January 19, 1946. It was the first successful radar contact with the Moon. The fourth and most spectacular recent event occurred on October 4, 1957. The "beep . . . beep . . . beeps" had announced to the world that man had established his first artificial Earth satellite.

These achievements someday will be recorded as the "four scientific wonders of the age," responsible for changing the course of human evolution. Together, they symbolize the accelerating force which is rapidly making the story of modern rocketry synonymous with the conquest of outer space. The outgrowth of these four symbols provides the foundations for this new world force . . . spacepower.

In order fully to grasp and understand the tremendous impact that spacepower will have on all of us, we must look to astronautics, one of the most important sciences of this new era. Our definition of astronautics would encompass "The science of man's movements and/or his instruments in the Universe." As such, astronautics covers many subdivisions, including anthropology, astronomy, astrophysics, space law, space medicine, space sociology, and space flight. It is this last area, "space flight," that is the most dramatic when considered in relation to the men, money, and material costs involved. Here is the vortex around which the other subdivisions revolve and obtain sustenance.

The fundamental concept of flight regimes (areas of flight) provides the operational zones of space flight. The first space-flight regime and currently the most discussed is the zone known as contiguous space.

Contiguous space flight is defined as including all flights outside the Earth's sensible atmosphere, describing their mission within the Earth-Moon system.

This fundamental concept of flight regimes provides us with the means for defining the remaining three zones of space flight:

Interplanetary space flight is defined as including all flights describing their mission within the Solar System, specifically on a planetary basis.

Interstellar space flight is defined as including all flights describing their mission within the Milky Way, specifically between star systems.

Intergalactic space flight is defined as including all flights describing their mission within the Universe, specifically between galactic systems.

It is significant to note that within the framework of our definition of space flight, the first flight regime, contiguous space, has been a basic zone for manned and unmanned research since the early flights of the V-2 and the Bell experimental rocket-powered aircraft. In addition, interplanetary space flight has been technically feasible for some time but has been lacking only in mission requirements and project funding. Lastly, man's ultimate challenge, the interstellar and intergalactic flight regimes, holds a visionaries' promise for the future.

But it is the first step of man's extension into the Universe, contiguous space flight, that we need to be predominantly concerned with now. In order to establish a background and understanding of today's events—the political, military and social implications of sputnik, controversial rocket programs and who is ahead of whom in what missile race—the authors will discuss first the highlights of rocketry, yesterday and today. Then, by extrapolation from the past and present, the authors will try to prognosticate where "rocketry tomorrow" will lead man in his evolution into space. This book will also cover the fundamentals of space sociology and space law and their relation to this new environment. In addition, the social impact of long-range missiles and Earth satellites on the world will also be covered. And finally, the organization, functions, and merits of a United Nations Space Program and an Educational Program for the space world of tomorrow will be considered.

All these concepts—together and not apart—make up the bedrock of *spacepower*.

THE AUTHORS
BALTIMORE, MD.
FEBRUARY, 1958

SPACEPOWER

chapter 1

why go into space?

The time is bound to come when man will venture ever
deeper into space—not to win wars but to battle the
limitless challenge of the universe.

Gen. Thomas S. Power
Commander in Chief, Strategic Air Command
Astronautics magazine, January, 1958

REGARDLESS of WHO you are, WHERE you are
and WHAT you are, with the advent of sputnik I, on October
4, 1957, you became part of a great adventure and new world
force—spacepower. For the first time in your evolution, you can
seriously contemplate leaving this planet, as we have the means
for doing so.

This new challenge of space and spacepower has rocked the
United States as few other events in the country's brief history.
In the present technological revolution focused on SPACE, we
find ourselves going through our fifth major crisis as a nation.
One can only think of the First and Second World Wars, the
War Between the States and the Revolutionary War as being
in a comparable category of events that shook this nation to its
foundations. The present crisis may be more significant than all
the four previous war-crisis periods combined.

The way the United States acts as one of the two major world
leaders in this crisis may well determine the future of mankind
on Earth and in space. It is for this reason that it becomes doubly
important that all thinking Americans and peoples of the world
understand the true meaning of spacepower.

Although the realization of spacepower had to await the development of rocket power, the idea of going into space is not a new one. As soon as man realized that the Moon and planets were worlds comparable to his own, he believed that people lived on them and that someday he would be able to visit them. In fact, the first-known science fiction novel concerned with a voyage to the Moon was written almost two thousand years ago. The Greek Sophist and satirist, Lucian of Samosata, wrote the book called *Vera Historia* (*True History*).

The *Vera Historia* is primarily a fantasy adventure story. A ship and crew are caught up in a waterspout and hurled into space. The ship is deposited on the Moon. The first sighting of the Moon as described in the English translation (Oxford, 1634) is, "wee came in view of a great countrie in the aire, like to a shining Island." As might be expected, the Moon is inhabited.

Lucian's other book on space travel, *Icaromenippus*, has the hero of the story plan a voyage to the Moon and to the stars. In this story, the hero uses the wing of a vulture and one of an eagle to propel him to his celestial destinations. He decides to continue his trip to heaven, but the displeased gods return him to Earth.

Another classic Moon-travel story, the first to appear in English literature, was published in the days of Charles I. The book was written by Bishop Francis Godwin and was entitled *The Man in the Moone*. Godwin's hero, Domingo, according to the story, trained wild geese to pull him through the air in a chariot. One day, much to his dismay, he discovered that the geese, instead of going south for the winter, went to the Moon—and they were taking him with them.

Cyrano de Bergerac is credited with writing two stories about lunar journeys. In his stories, Cyrano used three modes of space travel. Two of these methods, the bottles filled with dew (because dew rises) and an iron car lifted by means of tossing up lodestones, were fantasy. The third means of transportation, a box with a large number of powder rockets attached to it, is significant. With this means of space propulsion, Cyrano hit on the right method for space flight—the reaction principle.

Probably the best known of the earliest space-flight stories is Jules Verne's *Trip Around the Moon*. This work is outstanding because of the accurate approach to space flight. Jules Verne knew that neither wings nor balloons were of any use in space. Accordingly, he replaced them by a "space gun" capable of firing a manned projectile to the Moon. Verne's brother-in-law, a professor of mathematics, was one of the many experts who aided him in designing his great cannon, the "Columbine." For example, Verne had his calculations of the cannon muzzle velocity requirements checked by astronomical experts. He also resorted to guncotton invented only shortly before, and he also utilized a rare metal, aluminum, for the construction of his three-man space ball. The walls of the ball were a foot thick. This story provided another link in the evolution of space travel by establishing that space flight was a matter of velocity.

In literature, space-flight voyages are imaginary, and their main purpose is to entertain. Today, however, the scientists and the engineers have fulfilled the early promises of the science fiction writers and have made space flight a reality. With these new developments, can man justify his physical space travels as conveniently and as easily as he did his imaginary travels? The authors think not. As soon as space flight became an engineering probability, a question was raised many times over by people in all walks of life, military as well as civilian—and that question was, "Why go into space?"

Unfortunately, this question means different things to different people at different times, and a precise answer cannot be given.

However, the question will not go begging. We believe that the justification for space travel will be found among one or many of the following reasons: *economic, psychological, political, military, scientific*, and *moral*. Specifically, at this time, only you can choose your answer to this omnipresent question.

In seeking detailed answers to this question, let us examine first the economic reasons for going into space.

The *economic* history of mankind is the chronicle of man's destruction of his natural resources. A destruction, which if al-

lowed to continue, will someday soon render this planet as dead
as the Moon . . . incapable of producing even the barest essentials to maintain life for its overcrowded inhabitants.

When that day comes, what will man do? Where will he go?
To outer space?

Space flight as an ultimate solution for survival is best supported by examining two of the prime destructive economic
forces of man on earth—misuse of lands and overpopulation—
and the part that they have played in the fight for human existence.

In every generation of recorded history, the misuse of lands
is evident in many ways and in many areas over the face of this
planet. It is evident in soil erosion and in the ruins of our sand-
buried ancient empires. It is also evident in the floods and in
the sharply contrasting manmade deserts.

For many years soil erosion was considered to be the by-product of an extremely dry era in an area completely lacking in
rain for considerable periods of time. History and science no
longer support this thesis. For example, there are many sections
in Asia, the Americas, the Mediterranean areas and Africa that
are in complete ruin as far as natural resources are concerned;
yet there is no historical record to support the geological drying
up of these areas. To the contrary, there is evidence in the form
of vines and olive groves, standing since Roman times, which
conclusively prove that weather alone was not to blame. To be
sure, nature took its toll, but man was the prime destructive
force. One of the keys to the cause of this destruction lies in the
study of demography and is a matter of record.

During Christ's time, the world's population was estimated
at 250,000,000 people; today this number has increased to
2,800,000,000, with the population still growing at the rate of
43,000,000 people per year. If the current population rate increase remains constant, then by the year 2000, the world's
population should reach slightly more than six billion or somewhat more than double the present number. With increased
medical benefits both prolonging life and cutting down on the
ravages of disease, there is a real danger now of the world's be-

WHY GO INTO SPACE?

MORAL

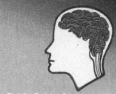

PSYCHOLOGICAL

ECONOMIC

SCIENTIFIC

POLITICAL

MILITARY

THE 6 COMPELLING REASONS

Plate 2

MAN IN SPACE

"WE MUST INITIATE A SPACE-FLIGHT PROGRAM WITH WHAT WE
HAVE TODAY AND PHASE OUR THINKING WITH THE TECHNOLOGICAL
AND ENVIRONMENTAL DEVELOPMENTS OF TOMORROW"

INTERPLANETARY SPACE

CONTIGUOUS SPACE

MANNED LUNAR EXPLO
CIRCUM. • LANDING • 1ST

UNMANNED LUNAR PROBES
LUNAR IMPACT / CIRCUMLUNAR / LUNAR LANDING

PERM

3-MAN SPACE
LIMITED TIME

2-MAN SPACE VEHICLE
MIN'MUM TIME ORBIT

RECOVERABLE BOOSTER
LAUNCHED

HIGH ENERGY CHEM.
BOOSTER LAUNCHED

CONVENT. CHEM.
BOOSTER LAUNCHED

RESEARCH A/C PROGRAM
AIR LAUNCHED

1958 1960 1965 1970 1975

Timetable

Fig. 1

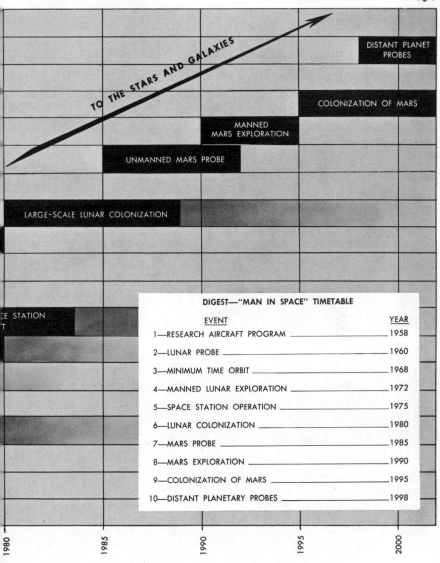

TO THE STARS AND GALAXIES

DISTANT PLANET PROBES

COLONIZATION OF MARS

MANNED MARS EXPLORATION

UNMANNED MARS PROBE

LARGE-SCALE LUNAR COLONIZATION

CE STATION

DIGEST—"MAN IN SPACE" TIMETABLE

EVENT	YEAR
1—RESEARCH AIRCRAFT PROGRAM	1958
2—LUNAR PROBE	1960
3—MINIMUM TIME ORBIT	1968
4—MANNED LUNAR EXPLORATION	1972
5—SPACE STATION OPERATION	1975
6—LUNAR COLONIZATION	1980
7—MARS PROBE	1985
8—MARS EXPLORATION	1990
9—COLONIZATION OF MARS	1995
10—DISTANT PLANETARY PROBES	1998

1980   1985   1990   1995   2000

SPACE TECHNOLOGY

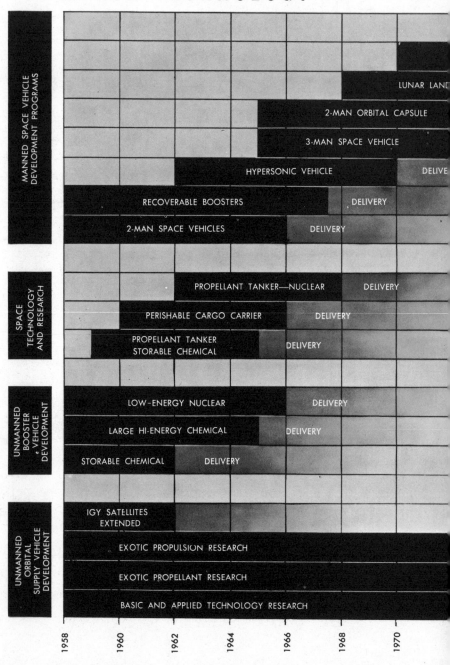

	MANNED SPACE VEHICLE DEVELOPMENT PROGRAMS						
							LUNAR LAND
					2-MAN ORBITAL CAPSULE	
				3-MAN SPACE VEHICLE		
		HYPERSONIC VEHICLE				DELIVE
RECOVERABLE BOOSTERS				DELIVERY		
2-MAN SPACE VEHICLES			DELIVERY			

SPACE TECHNOLOGY AND RESEARCH

PROPELLANT TANKER—NUCLEAR   DELIVERY

PERISHABLE CARGO CARRIER   DELIVERY

PROPELLANT TANKER STORABLE CHEMICAL   DELIVERY

UNMANNED BOOSTER & VEHICLE DEVELOPMENT

LOW-ENERGY NUCLEAR   DELIVERY

LARGE HI-ENERGY CHEMICAL   DELIVERY

STORABLE CHEMICAL   DELIVERY

UNMANNED ORBITAL SUPPLY VEHICLE DEVELOPMENT

IGY SATELLITES EXTENDED

EXOTIC PROPULSION RESEARCH

EXOTIC PROPELLANT RESEARCH

BASIC AND APPLIED TECHNOLOGY RESEARCH

1958   1960   1962   1964   1966   1968   1970

Timetable

Fig. 2

			COMMERCIAL TRANSPORT			DELIVERY		
DEEP-SPACE VEHICLE			DELIVERY					
		DELIVERY						
DELIVERY								
ERY								

DIGEST—"SPACE TECHNOLOGY" TIMETABLE

EVENT	DELIVERY YEAR
1—SPACE TECHNOLOGY RESEARCH	1958
2—FIRST LARGE-THRUST BOOSTER	1963
3—FIRST PROPELLANT TANKER	1964
4—FIRST SPACE VEHICLE	1966
5—FIRST RECOVERABLE BOOSTER	1967
6—HYPERSONIC ROCKET VEHICLE	1970
7—ORBITAL CAPSULE	1973
8—LUNAR FLEET	1977
9—ION VEHICLE	1980
10—COMMERCIAL TRANSPORT	1985

1974   1976   1978   1980   1982   1984   1986   1988

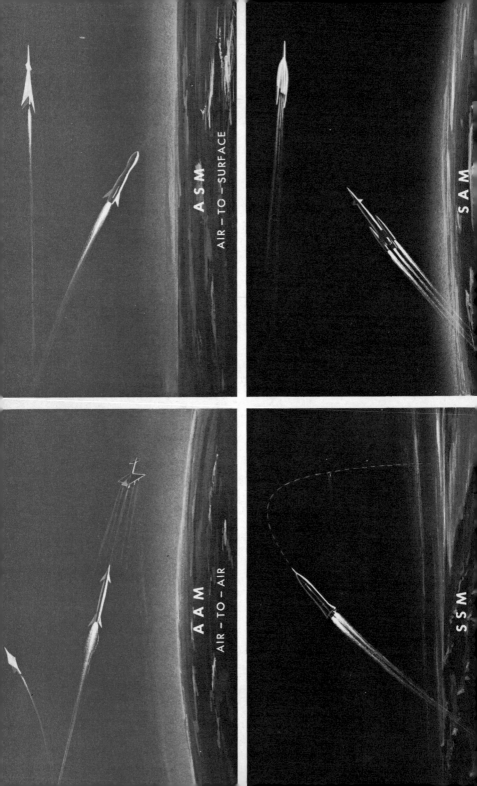

ASM
AIR-TO-SURFACE

SAM

AAM
AIR-TO-AIR

SSM

coming overpopulated in the near future. The U. S. Population Reference Bureau in December, 1957, stated that because of the rise in population there may be more poverty-stricken people in the world today than fifty to one hundred years ago.

Through the ages, man has been subjected to constant pressures to fulfill the immediate basic needs of the world's ever-increasing population. Because of the force of these pressures, which man often could not adequately meet, he followed an ancient pattern of land use—cut, burn, plant, destroy, move on—and has had little or no time to consider his legacy to future generations or how the Earth will sustain them.

This classical pattern of destruction of the Earth's natural resources has continued from the times of the ancient empires, through Africa, Europe, up to and including the discovery of the New World. No continents, nations, or peoples have been spared the cadence of this destructive process.

In the United States, for example, the search for new oil reserves has taken men far into the Pacific Ocean, the Gulf of Mexico, and now the Atlantic Ocean. This country has been one of the worst offenders in depleting our natural resources. Now it is desperately engaged in stockpiling many of these strategic lost items.

The effects of this practice were hardly noticeable when the world's population was limited. Land was plentiful, and time had an opportunity to heal the ravages of the system. However, with increasing populations, the growth of large cities, and the decrease in available lands, the long-term effects of this philosophy became more and more devastating. Wherever these two dynamic forces—misuse of lands and overpopulation—had been at work, history has recorded ruin and deterioration.

Let us now survey briefly the extent of this deterioration around the world and thereby try to evaluate its consequences which may eventually make "Exodus Earth" a necessity.

Starting with Egypt, historically one of the oldest countries, yet geologically the youngest, we have our first example of a deteriorating land. This nation, which, since the earliest generations, has depended for its existence upon the Nile and the productivity of the soil which was carried to it by the river's annual floods, is now undergoing two changes which may spell ruin to its sole source of survival.

The first of these changes is found in the nation's desire to increase the productivity of its crops. To achieve this, year-round irrigation was substituted for the flood-time irrigation which had been practiced for many centuries. The unceasing demands of year-round irrigation is steadily yet rapidly causing complete soil deterioration, especially since this new concept has done away with the annual five-month fallow period.

The second and still more important change is the destruction of forests at the source of the Nile, i.e., in Kenya, Uganda, and Ethiopia. Since the Nile now flows for 1,600 miles without receiving a single tributary, destruction of its watershed would mean eventual destruction of the Nile itself. If these two changes should come to pass, then we can expect the Nile Valley to become a completely barren waste such as the Egyptian desert is now.

The deterioration of lands in central Asia is attributed directly to the nomad bands which for hundreds of years have traveled from region to region. Wherever these bands stopped, destruction followed. The animals would overgraze, and the nomads themselves would add to this destruction by clearing wooded areas of shrubs and trees for shelter and firewood.

This practice today is largely controlled by the Soviet Government. It is attempting to settle these bands in permanent regions and is enforcing good grazing practices.

The problems in eastern Asia are in direct contrast to those of central Asia—here we have the more acute problem of overpopulation. The pressure of overpopulation is being met at the expense of the land—a land already in the advanced stages of erosion and deterioration. How will these many millions of people be fed? This is one of the most pertinent questions of the day for which there seems to be no answer.

China's problems are indicative of the kind that other nations will be faced with in the very near future, those of China being the more pressing at present because of her great population.

India is certainly one of the nations having population and soil problems. In fact, in some respects, her situation is graver than China's. The problem is still too many people for the land to support—again a land that has long since been depleted. India is an extreme example of the pressures of an ever-increasing population and misused lands which cannot support the people.

The Mediterranean Basin and the lands adjacent to it are not better off than are the people of Asia.

Greece, once the center of civilization—a region which abounded in natural resources and in which beautiful cities were built and great men lived in a creative atmosphere for centuries—is today an old, tired, wornout land with less than one cultivable acre per inhabitant. This acreage is hardly adequate, since 2.5 acres are required to sustain one person.

Areas in central and southern Africa have more recently become the victims of soil erosion and land deterioration. Africa illustrates graphically the adverse effects of a transplanted culture, specifically, European techniques of land utilization, and is a living witness that although these techniques may be highly successful in one region or climate, it does not necessarily follow that they will be successful in all regions and climates. In fact, in Africa's case, they proved exceedingly harmful.

The late Prime Minister of the Union of South Africa, Jan Smuts, once observed that "erosion is the biggest problem confronting the country, bigger than any politics."

One land area on the face of the Earth that has escaped the ravages of time is Western Europe. Fertile land well taken care of, ample rain, and the benefit of orderly seasons seem to have been the major reasons for this preservation.

Not all parts of Europe have fared so well. One illustration of erosion in Europe in historic times is the Pontine Marshes, the coastal area of Italy. Destruction of this once fertile farm area was the by-product of overpopulation and poor cultivation practices. This region had to be abandoned because of the salt that washed down from the surrounding mountain slopes which were poorly cultivated—in time the coastal area became a ma-

larial swamp, unfit for human habitation, which caused population jams inland.

Spain is unique because its land deterioration came about
more through greed than need. The history of its deterioration
process dates back to the time when Spain was once a powerful and prosperous nation.

Before the 15th century there existed an influential group of
sheepherders known as the Mesta. The Mesta, in order to feed
their flocks, moved them northward in the summer and south-
ward in the winter. Laws of the day prohibited them to graze
their flocks on lands belonging to villages which they passed on
their migrations. However, when Ferdinand and Isabella came
into power, they saw in the wool industry a great potential source
of wealth. Consequently, they re-enacted laws favoring this industry, and practically all lands were opened to the Mesta for
grazing purposes. Thus, flagrant overgrazing of the land caused
extreme erosion and consequent devastation.

The nomad invasion of Eastern Europe was still another
source of land destruction. The historian Gibbon once said of
the Mongols: "From the Caspian to the Indies they ruined a
tract of many hundred miles, and five centuries have not been
sufficient to repair the ravages of four years."

The two great oceans that protected the New World from the
destruction of two world wars were no barrier in sparing it from
the attack on its natural resources. The waste and destruction
of the Old World were in many respects a prelude to the destruction of the natural resources which followed in the New
World.

In Central and South America, growing population pressures
combined with misuse of lands fostered conditions that are un-
paralleled in their seriousness. The Pan American Union, after
a two-year field study, has characterized South America as the
vanishing continent.

The story of Mexico today, with certain variations, is comparable to the tragedy of the Mayan Empire and is indicative
of what is happening in most of the countries below the Rio
Grande. Mexico's plight was very vividly described by a distin-

guished Italian botanist with a thorough knowledge of southern Mexico. He stated that the State of Oaxaca will be a desert within fifty years. The Chief of the Conservation Section of the Pan American Union believes that within one hundred years the country will only be able to feed its people at the barest subsistence level. It can truthfully be said that Mexico, today, is fighting a losing battle for survival.

Surveys of Guatemala, El Salvador, and Venezuela show similar trends. Chile and Argentina can also be added to the long list of areas that have deteriorated or are in the process of doing so.

An interesting fact about the United States and Russia is that both countries have about the same amount of land suitable for agriculture in relation to their respective populations. Both countries are faced with an acute need for good conservation practices. The degree to which such measures are taken will aid to determine which nation will survive the other.

Fairfield Osborn in his book, *Our Plundered Planet*, wrote: "The time for generalizations, such as the third of the Four Freedoms, is over. 'Freedom from Want' is an illusory hope unless its pronouncement is coupled with a statement that clearly sets forth the present problem, so that all peoples everywhere may join in common endeavor to resolve it. The tide of the earth's populatioin is rising, the reservoir of the earth's living resources is falling. Technologists may outdo themselves in the creation of artificial substitutes for natural subsistence, and new areas, such as those tropical or subtropical regions, may be adapted to human use, but even such resources or developments, cannot be expected to offset the present terrific attack upon the natural life-giving elements of the earth. There is one solution: Man must recognize the necessity of cooperating with nature. He must temper his demands and use and conserve the natural living resources of the earth in a manner that alone can provide for the continuation of his civilization. The final answer is to be found only through comprehension of the enduring process of nature."

Let us emphasize that man must learn to co-operate with nature or his only recourse is "Exodus Earth."

Now that we have examined the long-range economic problems of human life on Earth itself, let us look briefly at some of the economic benefits of space flight—as it applies to the Earth directly.

There are immediate economic benefits that will accrue with the advent of fast rocket transportation between continents. This application of space flight awaits only the development of a more efficient rocket-propulsion system. When the high-efficiency system is made available, passengers, cargo, and mail can be whirled through the fringes of space from one distant point on the Earth to another in a matter of minutes. This fact should help to make the world a more tightly knit planet on which to live.

The more rapid transportation and communication which rockets could provide should help to give balance to the world's economy, particularly in rectifying the disparaging relationships between the present have and have-not nations. When shortages in raw materials, industrial or food products occur, the needed supplies can be quickly brought from surplus stockpile areas to those trouble spots where the need is the greatest.

No longer will we have to rely on slow-moving ships or railroads, trucks or airplanes to transport vital medical supplies to stricken areas in times of great natural catastrophes. Rocket relief ships can be dispatched to such places within an hour to relieve suffering as it occurs. In this important aspect of the world's economy, space flight can become a welcome boon from the heavens to those unfortunate ones on the Earth to help them in times of their greatest need.

The New York Times, on December 5, 1957, in a significant editorial entitled, "Man Into Space" classically summarizes the economic reasons for going into space by writing that "the basic lesson of the history of science is that all advance in scientific knowledge is ultimately transmuted into concrete advances of the greatest economic importance to all humanity. There is no reason to suppose that the knowledge we shall gain as we penetrate farther into space will have any different consequences. It is in this broader perspective that our national policy for the conquest of space must be planned."

With this glimpse into the predominant, compelling, economic reasons for expanding the space-flight program, let us look at some of the other reasons that are also important in considering "Why we want to go there." These reasons will be examined under the five categories of psychological, political, military, scientific, and moral aspects. Individually and collectively, they support and affect the economic reason.

Psychological reasons for going into space are many and complex. We can analyze the psychological motivation to escape from the Earth by examining the effects on individual men and then the propaganda effect on groups of men and society.

Why should man want to get away from a seemingly safe haven here on Earth where he still has not explored his natural surroundings completely? True, he has climbed the highest mountain at last, but there are still many mountains and the depths of the oceans, as well as remote polar places that remain to be explored. Probably the best expression of the lure of the unconquered on man was the classic statement of George Leigh-Mallory, who sacrificed his life in a heroic attempt to be the first man to scale Mount Everest successfully. He was asked why he sought to climb the impossible and forbidding summit, and his simple and enduring retort was, "Because it's there."

Supreme Court Justice, William O. Douglas, world traveler and mountain climber himself, seconded Mallory and added that mountains are "a challenge that . . . give[s] you a strange exhilaration and . . . a feeling of achievement." These same feelings of compulsion may be transferred to the men who wish to volunteer as the world's first space travelers.

The personal curiosity and lure of the unknown drives men to seek the answers to the riddles of the Universe. The same drive that propelled Columbus or Magellan is present today in the many men (and women) of all nations who seek not just to escape from the problems on Earth but, by their exploration, hope to solve the unanswered questions and scientific riddles of outer space.

The world in its days of creation was our first literal "spaceship." And the uncharted lands across the seas from Spain in 1492 were like the far uncharted reaches of space today. As Columbus was lured economically by hopes of finding gold, yet ended up discovering a far wealthier land worth more than all the gold which he might have found, so the first space explorers might find things in space that they originally had not foreseen when they first charted their courses to these distant destinations. But unlike Columbus, who took three months to discover America, or Magellan, who took years to circle the world, our first space explorers will require less than five days to reach the Moon. This knowledge will contribute to the peace of mind of our space travelers and eliminate the anxieties which plagued our early explorers. We know more today about our future trips to the distant planets and stars than world explorers of the past knew about their trips before they started out.

The psychological effect of space flight was most apparent in the tremendous impact of the first satellite on the world. Overnight, the complacent approach of the American people to many aspects of life, and the role of the United States in the world changed drastically. Cries of a "technological Pearl Harbor" were heard throughout the land, and even though a few politicians spoke of sputnik as a "silly bauble," or a "nice scientific trick," the majority of the leaders reacted favorably to the psychological shock, and the gears of democracy started to work to correct the deficiencies which led to the Soviet victory of establishing the first Earth satellite.

It was recognized that every day the Soviets had a satellite in orbit, and the United States did not, their prestige increased in the eyes of the rest of the world.

Each succeeding instrument launched into space by any nation gives it a psychological edge in the international chess game. Whoever first sends up a rocket into orbit with an animal aboard (ultimately a man), and brings the creature back alive, will gain a tremendous advantage over all the other nations of the world.

Major General Bernard A. Schriever, the head of the Air Force Ballistic Missile Division, commented on the psychological reasons for going into space when he said, "Our prestige as a world leader might well dictate that we undertake lunar expeditions and even interplanetary flight when the approximate chronological advances have been made, and the time is ripe."

The time is ripe now!

The *political* benefits of going into space will accrue to the nations that get there first. The prestige which was accorded Russia for her scientific advances symbolized by her satellites was immediately transmitted to the political councils of the world. Many of the neutral nations, particularly in southeast Asia and Africa, soon leaned noticeably toward the Soviet as a result of sputnik.

So, a new political balance of power was evident after sputnik. Less than a month after the launching of her first satellite on October 4, 1957, the Russians pulled out of the deliberations of the United Nations Disarmament Commission. Even our own Secretary of State, John Foster Dulles, warned in a news conference on November 5, 1957, that the United States cannot expect to enjoy the preponderance of power it had a decade ago.

This was a startling admission from the second-highest political figure in the land, coming as it did on top of earlier statements that there was no great political significance in the satellite launchings. With the political impact of the first crude unmanned satellites being so obviously significant, it is little wonder what greater impact larger, manned satellites and spaceships will have on the balance of power in the world. It was this reason above all others that was probably behind President Eisenhower's decision to make his television chats to the nation on national security.

Heretofore, only the three traditional elements of military power—the Army, Navy, and Air Force—were looked upon as a necessary attribute of political power. The sum of the force of these three bodies in any one nation added or detracted from its political power around the diplomatic tables.

Now a fourth form of quasi-military and scientific power—spacepower—has entered upon the scene and must be considered along with its older sisters in any assessment of a nation's total political power.

A nation which lags behind in the conquest of space becomes a second-rate power politically. The relative status of any one nation at any given moment in its attempts to penetrate space is a test of its political leadership on the surface. Underneath, it symbolizes the degree of its scientific achievement and the health of its educational system.

The sputniks sealed the coffin on the United States "containment" theory which is now as antiquated as the Maginot line and the horse cavalry. Since satellites can go over the Iron Curtain and Western national barriers at will, they have caused a drastic "new look" in foreign policy to be undertaken by the United States and its Allies. Although the satellites scheduled for launching during the IGY are peaceful scientific instruments, the portent of things to come, particularly future reconnaissance satellites, has led to a political re-evaluation in the West.

The sputniks performed a political service to the West, which no other event since the Suez tragedy of late 1956 had been able to accomplish. It bound the Western nations together politically and militarily for the first time in over a year—and at a time when they were in danger of splintering asunder. Our great hope is that space flight can foster and bring about political unity—not only among the friendly North Atlantic Treaty Organization powers, as the sputniks have certainly accomplished, but ultimately between the Goliaths, the United States and Russia.

Another reason for an "Exodus Earth" program is the *military* one. Right after sputnik, military leaders, politicians, and columnists prognosticated on the size and characteristics of the Soviet vehicle which apparently had propelled the satellite into space. It was the underlying fear and awe of the success of the Soviet satellite rocket launcher, while the United States was still trying to perfect its own, that pointed up the significance of the military impact of sputnik. The Soviet has literally forced this country into space, whether it wishes to follow or not. The

Soviets are calling the shots in the race for space. The national security of the United States demands that so long as there is a race into space between nations it must not only catch up with but surpass the Soviets.

Statements were made after sputnik in both the United States and Russia concerning the building of larger unmanned military satellites, such as reconnaissance vehicles which will be able to photograph many parts of the Earth several times a day and send televised pictures back to the sending nation. Satellites containing nuclear weapons which can be ejected at a certain point in their orbits to return to Earth pose another military possibility for utilizing these first space instruments.

Then there is the vision of some military planners of establishing a manned military space station, first in an orbit around the Earth to act as a surveillance weapon, and later on the Moon, itself. Whichever nation can get to the Moon first with the "most" and has the capability of *returning to any spot on Earth* possesses an overwhelming military and psychological advantage over have-not nations who cannot go there and back. Knowing that someone is there and not having the ability to intercept or reach him can alter the military balance of power on the Earth below more drastically than any superterrestrial weapons system that man may devise. Military satellites are also seen as potential bases for launching missiles with atomic warheads. Professor Hermann Oberth, the father of astronautics, has proposed that a giant mirror in space (some sixty miles in diameter) could be used militarily to burn an enemy country on Earth. For peaceful purposes, however, such a space mirror could be used to melt icebergs and alter temperatures.

There are two major *scientific* reasons why the United States and its Allies must go into space: the first, and probably the most important, reason is that space represents the world's new scientific frontier for fundamental research, which Michael Faraday suggested, ". . . instead of exhausting the subject of research, opens the door to further and more abundant knowledge, overflowing with beauty and utility"; and secondly, that the establishment of the first manmade Earth satellite by the Soviet

scientists and engineers constitutes a direct scientific challenge
from Russia to the Free World.

Behind this challenge lies a threat not only to the very existence of the United States but also to that of the Free World itself. It was a well-known fact that the Soviet set about years ago
to surpass the United States, and therefore the Free World, in
all fields of the basic sciences.

The present Soviet technological position has been achieved
under the combined influence of an ever-mounting pressure
from a series of Russian rulers. This position is a matter of scientific history and tradition. During the regimes of Ivan the Ter-
rible, Peter the Great, and Catherine the Great, large financial
grants were made to support research and the study of the basic
sciences. The Soviet Union, the heir to this great tradition, recognized its potential and made education and science a major part
of its five-year programs.

The technical improvement doctrines initiated by Lenin were
carried on and expanded by Stalin at a tremendous cost. Through
the years, there have been many evidences of this "do or die"
philosophy at work. It was evident in Russia's accomplishments
in the field of physics, and her atomic energy and "plasma" programs. It was also evident in such key fields as mathematics,
chemistry, and aerodynamics.

These were unmistakable and unheeded signs to the Free
World nations that their position in the basic and applied sciences no longer remained unchallenged.

Never before in their short history have the Soviets demonstrated in such absolutely unmistakable terms the symbols of
their new-found technical strength as they did in the establishment of the first manmade Earth satellite. This is the core of
the scientific challenge today—in the fields of basic research and
science and not just the sputniks and the muttniks, which are
symbols among the fruits of that research. However, we should
not overlook the scientific benefits of satellites, which were
best summed up by Dr. Fred Whipple, the head of the Smithsonian Observatory at Harvard, who said shortly after sputnik
had been launched, that "we have learned more in the past ten

days about astronomy than we have learned in the past 200 years."

Morally, we need to ensure that the first penetrations into space be undertaken in a sane, ethical manner, so as to prevent a repetition of events that took place on Earth when the Old World empires were struggling toward their former power pinnacles.

Let us hope that man may not make the same mistakes with his new-found freedom in space travel that he did with his greedy plundering of the then unknown worlds from the 16th century to the present. His record during the last five and one-half centuries, particularly in the newer, civilized countries, has been largely an amoral one in his treatment of nature and his fellow man.

There is a larger moral question which may arise when we discover that we are not the only humans living in the Universe. Dr. Harlow Shapley, a famous Harvard astronomer, declares that we are not alone in the Universe, with possibly over 100 million planets in our galaxy capable of supporting life as we know it. The curiosity of finding out what this life is like will continue to nag space pioneers and motivate them toward further travels.

When and if we do discover other forms of human life in the Universe, the follow-up question arises. How will the space traveler from Earth react when he meets the first being from another planet? Will his moral values permit him to treat his opposite according to the principle of the Golden Rule, or will man revert to his former nature that he has never quite outgrown? His initial actions at this historic first meeting may well determine the course of man's future in space.

Lack of means to communicate in a common language will be a terrific barrier to establishing the proper rapport with creatures from other planets in our star system or far-distant star systems. Whenever and wherever this meeting occurs, man will be faced with the greatest moral challenge of his lifetime.

In his escape from Earth, he can start with a really clean slate when he sets foot for the first time on other planets, moons, and—someday—other star systems. He can never escape from himself but only from his past environment. Yet, it is highly probable that as man penetrates deeper and deeper into space, his moral values will become strengthened because of the realization of his own insignificance.

We have examined six of the many possible reasons that man might use to justify his desire to go into space. It is essential to understand that once one becomes persuaded that these reasons for going into space are entirely justified, then the major programs presented in the latter chapters of this book become more feasible. These programs center about the need for the establishment of a United Nations Space Force, an International Lunar Project and Space Program, and an adequate Space World Education Program.

This book attempts to justify the immediate need for a pay-as-you-go astronautics program under United Nations sponsorship, with a challenge to the political leaders of the world to back such a long-range plan now. The hidden bonus effect of the inauguration of a comprehensive space program could very well be . . . peace on Earth. For one soon realizes that with the advances in modern weapons technology, global thermonuclear wars on Earth would mean mutual suicide of civilization as we know it.

Space, therefore, becomes the only battleground left for major wars of the future between nations of the Earth. Instead, let us hope and plan that it will provide the fertile frontier for man's peaceful evolution into the Universe.

Now let us look back to the beginnings of rocketry and trace the development of the state-of-the-art in rocketry to the present, so that we may better understand why it is possible today seriously to consider going into space.

chapter 2

rocketry yesterday

The subject of projection from the Earth, and especially a
mention of the moon, must still be avoided in dignified
scientific and engineering circles, even though projection
over long distances on the earth's surface no longer calls
for quite so high an elevation of eyebrows.

Dr. Robert H. Goddard
A Method of Reaching Extreme Altitudes—1919

THE underlying developments which led to the present state-of-the-art in rocketry are the results of a combined
effort of many nations and peoples. Three main periods can be
distinguished in the development process: the first period extends
from antiquity to A.D. 1242 and Roger Bacon's introduction
of *De Mirabili Potestate Artis et Naturae* (*On the Marvelous
Powers of Art and Nature*); the second period covers Sir Isaac
Newton's Laws of Motion through the time of Sir William Congreve's rockets (1670 to 1826); and the third period includes the
publication of Goddard's *A Method of Reaching Extreme Altitudes* through to the present (1919–58).

In the first period, man learned how to make gunpowder and
how to use the propulsive characteristics of this rapidly burning
compound. In the second period, we saw not only the beginnings of science in rocketry, but we also witnessed the large-
scale development and utilization of war rockets. In the third
period, with the impetus of the Second World War, we saw the
rocket develop from its previously limited role of an artillery
rocket to that of a multipurpose weapon and research tool.

In these three periods, many famous names in history and science appear: in the first, Hero of Alexandria and Roger Bacon; in the second, Sir Isaac Newton and Sir William Congreve; and in the third appear such contributors as Konstantin E. Ziolkovsky and Nikolai A. Rynin of Russia; Hermann Oberth, Max Valier, Eugen Sänger, Wernher von Braun of Germany; Robert Esnault-Pelterie of France; and Dr. Robert H. Goddard of the United States.

These are the events and the giants around which the present historical sketch will be developed. It is intended to show how these talented visionaries and their disciples have made A *Method of Reaching Extreme Altitudes* possible.

The story of modern rocketry had its beginnings before the birth of Christ, the exact origin of which is lost in legend and antiquity. Historically, the recorded use of saltpeter (potassium nitrate) by primitive Eastern tribes, for curing meat, provides us with our first link in the evolution of propulsion and rocketry. The gunpowder potential of this ancient household item was very likely discovered accidentally at the time when some of it was dropped into a fire—resulting in a bright flash flame. These flame-supporting properties no doubt were responsible for man trying to combine saltpeter with wood for fire making. Since sawdust or fine wood particles were not available, the saltpeter was evidently added to charcoal. Saltpeter and charcoal are two of the three constituents that make up gunpowder.

In this period, there is no record that sulfur, the final constituent, was ever added to this mixture to make gunpowder. It is certain, however, that a composition containing the first two constituents, known as "Chinese Fire," was used long before the time of Christ. It is equally well-known that propulsion properties of this mixture were not recognized until after the time of Christ. The utilization of Chinese Fire for propulsive purposes probably developed initially as a result of its use in hollow bamboo rods or arrows. It must have been accidentally observed that the bamboo rods and arrows had a tendency to propel themselves due to the burning and expansion of gases through the rod.

Another important link in the evolution of rocketry is the demonstration in A.D. 160, of the aeolipile (named after Aeolus, the god of winds) by Hero of Alexandria, a Greek mathematician and scientist. Basically, the aeolipile consisted of a hollow sphere mounted so that it could rotate between two supports. These supports in turn carried steam from a closed container which was suspended over a fire. The rotating sphere had two right-angle pipes located 180 degrees apart on the sphere. The steam jet escaping through the right-angle pipes or nozzles caused the sphere to revolve. The aeolipile is probably the first-known device used to demonstrate the jet-reaction principle.

The first reference to the rocket principle is recorded in a Chinese chronicle, *T-hung-kang-mu*, and that chronicle dates the first use of the reaction principle as occurring in A.D. 1232, during the Mongol siege to the city of Kai-fung-fu (Pien-king). During this siege the Chinese used two new weapons, the first, called "heaven-shaking thunder," had a bomblike function and was dropped from the walls of the city on the invaders; and the second, called "arrow of flying fire," is generally regarded as the first application of the rocket invention. The arrow of flying fire was probably an extension of the stuffed-bamboo-rod principle mentioned earlier and most likely consisted of a small package of the incendiary material tied to the arrow.

From this beginning, the use of gunpowder rockets grew rapidly, and the pyrotechnic art spread from Asia to the Middle East, to Europe and England.

Many descriptions of rocket making appear in chronicles written in the next few centuries. Much progress was evident in the pyrotechnic art and rocket design.

Roger Bacon, an English monk, was credited with the introduction of rockets into Europe prior to A.D. 1249. In his *De Mirabili Potestate Artis et Naturae*, Roger Bacon established the composition of gunpowder as follows: ". . . but of saltpeter take 7 parts, 5 of young hazel twigs, and 5 of sulphur; and so thou wilt call up thunder and destruction, if thou know the art."

In A.D. 1258 the first mention of a rocket in Europe appeared in the chronicle of Cologne, and, in 1379, an Italian historian credits a rocket with a significant victory in the battle for the Isle of Chiozza.

A German engineer, Konrad Kyeser von Eichstädt, experimented with gunpowder mixtures in 1405 and is credited with advancing the art of pyrotechnics.

A technical paper, entitled *Treatise upon Several Kinds of War Fireworks*, published in 1561 in France, describes the use of military rockets in the defense of Orleans against the English in 1429; during the siege of Pont-Andemer in 1449; against Bordeaux in 1452; and at Gand in 1453. This particular paper is significant in that the treatise suggests an alternate material for the rocket casings which up to that time were still bamboo. This bamboo technique was probably still the same one that had been used for 1,500 years.

In 1630, the rocket evolved in the form of a grenade, and in 1645, during the Thirty Years' War, the rocket was credited with the downfall of Phillipsburg, France.

In 1668, Col. Friedrich von Geissler, a German, conducted the first purely scientific research in rocketry. His papers indicated that both propellants and rocket case characteristics had been evaluated for two rockets. Successful propellant experiments were conducted on a 55-pound and 132-pound rocket utilizing wooden rocket cases reinforced with linen.

In the latter part of the 17th century, Sir Isaac Newton opened the third period of rocketry when he interpreted and correlated many diverse observations in mechanics and combined the results into three fundamental laws known as Newton's Laws of Motion. These laws simplified the science of mechanics and the Third Law formed the basis of modern rocketry. The Third Law states: "For every action there is an equal and opposite reaction, and the two are along the same straight line." Such a reaction must take place anywhere under any conditions—underwater, in the air, or in a vacuum. In fact, many people today still believe that a rocket goes forward by "pushing against the air."

The early 18th century saw the use of the military rocket die out, although its use in pyrotechnics was continued.

In the accounts of the India Campaign in the latter part of the 18th century (1792–99), we again find interest in the military rocket. At this time British forces in India were defeated, with severe losses, by an opposing Indian rocket force of 5,000 men. In this campaign, the rocket case had gone through still another step in its evolution. It was now made of iron, being some 8 inches long by 1.5 inches in diameter. However, the rocket still carried an 8-foot-long stick stabilizer.

It was at this time that Sir William Congreve became interested in the military rocket. His experiments at the Royal Laboratory at Woolwich resulted in several successful military rockets—with ranges up to 2,000 yards.

During the European wars of the early 19th century, these rockets were successfully employed against Boulogne (1806), Copenhagen (1807), and Danzig (1813). Just about this time, two other payload applications for the rocket were found, namely bomb carrying and shrapnel.

By this time the military rocket had become so popular that, in 1817, the British Army formed the Field Rocket Brigade. The rocket brigade took part in virtually every important battle against Napoleon and distinguished itself particularly well in the final battle at Waterloo. Probably Congreve's rockets are best-known for their use against Fort McHenry which inspired Francis Scott Key to write the immortal lines—"the rockets' red glare, the bombs bursting in air"—as part of our national anthem, "The Star-Spangled Banner."

The evolution and utilization of the Congreve rockets were milestones in the development of rocketry. First, they were developed as an incendiary rocket which had limited military value. Then the rocket was given a greater destructive capability when bomb and shrapnel-type warheads were employed. Finally, rocket stabilization in flight, by the application of jet vanes in the nozzle, increased the rocket's accuracy and consequently its utility as a military weapon. However, even with all these improvements, by the end of the 19th century, military rockets had again become obsolete and were replaced by the more accurate artillery gun.

In the early part of the 20th century modern rocket research began with the work of Dr. Robert H. Goddard. Dr. Goddard, backed by a small grant from the Smithsonian Institution, directed a group in research and development of military rockets during World War I. The group was successful, and a demonstration was held at the Aberdeen Proving Grounds on the 6th and 7th of November, 1918. The reports from these demonstrations were so encouraging that the Government authorized limited rocket research between World War I and World War II.

It was not generally known, however, in or out of the United States, until 1919, that Dr. Goddard was engaged in rocket research and development. At that time, Goddard delivered his now-famous monograph to the Smithsonian Institution called, A *Method of Reaching Extreme Altitudes*. In the second part of this paper, in addition to the report of his experimental work, Dr. Goddard showed that a rocket with a gross weight of 22,000 pounds would be capable of escaping from the Earth and delivering a payload of magnesium powder to the Moon. He estimated that in impacting on the Moon a flash could be created which would be visible on the Earth. It is interesting to note that the Vanguard launching vehicle weighs 22,000 pounds and secondly, many people today are proposing that we send nuclear or other type warheads to the Moon to create an explosion which would be visible on Earth.

In addition to his high-altitude research, development of rockets, and theoretical studies for placing a payload on the Moon, there is evidence to support the assumption that Goddard recognized the potential of rocketry in space flight. In his monograph, A *Method of Reaching Extreme Altitudes*, he suggests, *"There are, however, developments of the general method under discussion which involve a number of important features not herein mentioned, which could lead to results of much scientific interest. These developments involve many experimental difficulties, to be sure, but they depend upon nothing that is really impossible."* (Goddard's italics.)

By 1926, Dr. Goddard's research activities included almost every aspect of rocket design and culminated in a feasibility demonstration of the world's first liquid-propellant rockets. Although the demonstration was successful, his accomplishments were ahead of their time and not immediately recognized.

Dr. Goddard continued his research first in New England and then later in the deserts of New Mexico. Many experimental rocket-stabilization flights were conducted in New Mexico. On December 30, 1930, an 11-foot rocket reached a height of 2,000 feet and a velocity of 500 miles per hour. Another flight, on March 28, 1935, achieved a height of 4,800 feet and a velocity of 550 miles per hour. Subsequent rocket firings achieved altitudes of 7,500 feet and speeds of 700 miles per hour.

Some of Dr. Goddard's contributions to rocketry, of which there were many, were as follows:

1. Mathematical analysis of multistage rockets.
2. Feasibility of liquid propellants.
3. Centrifugal propellant pump.
4. The use of jet vane fins in the rocket exhaust.
5. Invented the first practical gyroscope.

Goddard is truly the father of modern rocketry. In 1922, Hermann Oberth wrote to Goddard, requesting a copy of *A Method of Reaching Extreme Altitudes*. The following year, Oberth published his classical book on space travel, *Die Rakete zu den Planetenräumen* (*The Rocket to the Interplanetary Spaces*). This book, written by a mathematician, discussed in great detail the theoretical requirements for contiguous and interplanetary space travel. The book brought adverse comments from the uninformed and praise from the disciples. Subsequent publication supporting Oberth's thesis was Dr. Walter Hohmann's book, *Die Errechbarkeit der Himmelskörper* (*The Attainability of the Celestial Bodies*). This book was a highly theoretical treatment of minimum energy departure trajectories from the Earth and return to the Earth from the other planets. This was followed by Max Valier's *Der Vorstoss in den Weltraum* (*A Dash Into Space*). These classics were the forerunners of the many publications which followed on the feasibility of space flight.

In 1929, Hermann Oberth published his most important work, *Die Wege zur Raumschiffahrt* (*The Roads to Space Travel*). In this book Oberth presented a most complete analysis of contiguous and interplanetary space flight. He discussed in great detail the problems associated with the design of manned space vehicles and flights in these zones. He also covered the possibility of artificial satellites.

As a direct result of Oberth's publications, the German Society for Space Travel (*Verein für Raumschiffahrt*) was formed.

The German Rocket Society for the advancement of space travel was organized in 1929. After going through a period of natural growth, i.e., developing a unity of purpose and procuring test facilities, the group was successful in developing a number of liquid rockets. In 1933, the military, after witnessing a formal rocket demonstration by the society, commissioned one of the society members, Wernher von Braun, then aged twenty-four, to develop an experimental military rocket.

In twelve short years (1933–45), the German military rocket research program had gone through an amazing period of development. Rocket research had progressed from the A-1 in 1933, weighing 330 pounds, which was never fired, to the famous A-4, commonly known as the V-2, weighing 24,000 pounds. Approximately 1,120 V-2's were fired on England, with 1,050 actually falling on London, and 2,500 were fired against other targets in Europe. To make the total complete, it should be mentioned that probably another thousand V-2's were fired for training purposes, and still hundreds more were brought to the United States for research.

Advanced thinking and planning had also gone into the A-10, a two-stage missile which would extend the range of the A-4 across the Atlantic.

To carry out this accelerated military rocket program, the Peenemünde Research Institute had been established in 1937 on the Baltic seacoast by the German Army. These facilities, which have long since become as famous as the rocket produced there, were very short-lived. In the early months of 1945, the Peenemünde facilities were captured by Russian armies.

Thus it appears that after 700 years of rocketry, it remained for the German scientists and engineers to inject successfully the principle of the "arrow of flying fire" into practically every level of their military weapons system. Dr. Walter Dornberger, former Commandant of Peenemünde, sums up what he believes to be Peenemünde's major contributions to rocketry as follows: "We developed rocket propulsion to a practically unimagined level of performance, applied high speed aerodynamics on a big scale and gave guidance techniques the dominant place in our work that properly belonged to it. The long range rocket owes its birth no less to the intelligent exploitation of these three new branches of technology than to skill, enthusiasm, and cooperation of the men engaged in the project."

chapter 3

rocketry today

The present state of science and of technological knowledge permits the building of machines that can rise beyond the limits of the atmosphere of the earth.

After further development these machines will be capable of attaining such velocities that they—left undis-
turbed in the void of ether space—will not fall back to
earth; furthermore, they will even be able to leave the
zone of terrestrial attraction.

Hermann Oberth
Die Rakete zu den Planetenräumen—1923
(The Rocket to the Interplanetary Spaces)

SHORTLY before the capture of Peenemünde, in the
final phases of World War II, the United States, its Allies and
Russia realized that the Germans were way ahead of every nation in guided-missile development and application. Accordingly,
they organized teams of technical experts, both civilian and
military, to search the German research centers and factories
for information pertaining to rocket development. When the
European war ended, these technical teams proceeded to fulfill
their assigned tasks. As a direct result of this action, literally
tons of captured documents and all types of rocket hardware
were confiscated by the participating nations.

One very important part of this program was the search for
experienced rocket people. Of the thousands of technical personnel who worked at Peenemünde and other rocket-producing
facilities, it was reported that the Soviet central agency, whose

sole function was to recruit German rocket specialists after
World War II, rounded up a total of 5,000 scientists, engineers,
and technicians from the Peenemünde project. The United
States took under its wings a few big names but let the bulk of
the Peenemünde colony slip through its fingers to Russia. In
this manner, Russia acquired almost all of Hitler's best rocket
brains, and within an incredibly short period had them working
around the clock seven days a week on their rocket developments.

Thus, it was not until the capture of Peenemünde and the
roundup of its scientists, documents, and missiles that a guided-
missile program was initiated by some of the major nations of
the world. Since then, however, the status of worldwide guided-
missile programs indicates that Argentina, the British Commonwealth, Italy, Japan, France, Holland, Russia, Switzerland, Sweden, and the United States are actively engaged in a missile
technological race on a scale that has seen no precedent or
parallel in the course of human history. This missile race is
centered around four basic military categories (*see* Fig. 3)
which include: (1) air-to-air (AAM); (2) air-to-surface (ASM);
(3) surface-to-air (SAM); and (4) surface-to-surface (SSM)
missiles.

Let us examine in detail "rocketry today" and the results of
this twelve-year missile armament marathon.

Argentina

Argentina is the only known country in South America that
has entered the missile field. Its entry was with the AF3, a surface-to-surface missile developed for use against tanks, trucks,
and small ships.

British Commonwealth

The British Commonwealth's contributions to rocketry have
been the subject of many highly controversial debates in the
last few years. The authors believe that the most accurate ac-
count of the British achievements was recently expressed by Mr.

Leonard Bertin, Science Correspondent for *The London Daily Telegraph and Morning Post*, who, after touring major missile facilities in the British Isles and visiting the long-range missile test site in Woomera, Australia, stated: "With the limited resources it has available, England's missile development program is actually achieving a great deal."

The first concrete evidence supporting Mr. Bertin's opinion is the recent missiles data and photographic releases by the Ministry of Supply. This, coupled with announcement by The Society of British Aircraft Constructors (SBAC) that four hundred British companies are actively engaged in missile and development work, substantiates that the British Commonwealth is advancing steadily in missile development. In addition, at the Royal Aircraft Establishment, scientists are actively working on new concepts related to basic missile research. The Farnborough facility is known to have a well-equipped laboratory, including the TRIDAC guided-missile simulator, and the Hawker Siddeley Company has established one of the newer missile research facilities near Coventry.

Supporting these research and development centers are several test facilities. The Ministry of Supply has added a 200,000-pound propulsion test complex (facility) to supplement the many currently in existence at this center. Also scheduled for completion in 1958 is the Ministry of Defense's large new missile firing range at South Uist off the west coast of Scotland. To date, however, the only operating range in England is the 250-acre Aberporth facility on the Welsh coast. It is estimated that about 1,000 large test missiles are launched at this facility yearly in addition to the many hundreds of smaller vehicles such as target drones. Jodrell Bank, the world's largest radio telescope, is situated in England and plays a vital role in tracking missiles and satellites.

The best-known Anglo-Australian rocket test facility is the Woomera Range in Australia, the site at which the majority of Britain's missiles have been tested. The Woomera test site consists of a corridor that cuts across 1,200 desolate miles of Australia extending northwest to the shores of the Indian Ocean.

This test range can easily be increased to 2,700 miles by extending it to Christmas Island in the Indian Ocean.

Today, as during World War II, the major concern of the British is defense, and missiles have been chosen as the best means, as borne out by Defense Minister Duncan Sandys' announcement in April, 1957, that the English Electric P-1 is the last manned fighter; that Avro Vulcan B2 and the Handley Page Victor B2 are the last of the manned bombers; that all interception of enemy craft in defense of England will eventually be made by a single operational air-to-air missile, the Firestreak; that pending operational use of an intercontinental ballistic missile (ICBM), the range of the V-bombers would be increased by the use of an air-to-surface missile; and that because of the destructive capabilities of nuclear weapons, target defense will eventually be restricted to ICBM retaliation bases eliminating oldtime emphasis on populated area protection.

In support of this concept, England has developed or is in various stages of developing missiles in the basic four categories: air-to-air, air-to-surface, surface-to-air, and the ever-important, long-range, surface-to-surface missile.

In the air-to-air category, three missiles are of importance— the Fireflash, Firestreak, and the Red Dean. The performance of the Fireflash, the first operational missile in this category, grew out of World War II requirements of the Royal Air Force. The Fireflash is currently in use on the Supermarine Swift MK7, the Hawker Hunter, and the Avon Sabre fighters. The vehicle configuration is characteristic of many British vehicles in that it has wrap-around, solid-propellant boost motors.

It is significant to note that the wrap-around booster technique seems to be unique with the British. Normally, missile boosters are attached in tandem; i.e., the missile is placed on top of the booster. This arrangement leads to a long, slim vehicle configuration. Whereas, in the wrap-around configuration, the booster, usually in three or four pairs, is placed in parallel around the outside of the main rocket. This arrangement in turn leads to a short stubby rocket. In either case the boosters drop away after firing. It would be most difficult at this time to state that one technique is actually better than the other.

The second vehicle in this category, the Firestreak, is approximately 7 feet in length and somewhat larger than the Fireflash. It is propelled by a solid-propellant motor. Its range is 8 miles, and guidance is infrared, i.e., heat seeking. This missile is scheduled for use on the English Electric P-1 and the Gloster Javelin fighters. The Royal Navy will also use it with its DH Sea Vixens aircraft. The Red Dean, the third in the series, was being developed by Vickers-Armstrongs when it was rumored to have been canceled.

In the air-to-surface category only one missile is reported to be under development. The missile is expected to be comparable in size to the U. S. Air Force's Rascal, and its application is reported to be with the RAF's Vulcan and Victor bombers.

In the surface-to-air category there are three missiles, the Bloodhound, Thunderbird, and the Sea Slug. All are reported now in production. The Bloodhound is expected to be Britain's first operational missile in this category. The second most publicized missile in this family is the Thunderbird. Performance of this vehicle is said to be on the same order as the U. S. Nike Hercules. The Royal Navy's entry in this family is the Sea Slug, designed especially for naval defense. The missile configuration includes the wrap-around, solid-propellant boosters as well as a solid-propellant sustainer motor. It has medium-range interception capability and can reach any aircraft flight altitude necessary for interception.

The surface-to-surface family boasts of only one vehicle, a 2,000-mile intermediate range ballistic missile (IRBM). This vehicle has no known name at present. De Havilland in conjunction with Rolls Royce has prime responsibility for developing this missile for the RAF. The ICBM which was being developed by Vickers-Armstrongs was canceled for undisclosed reasons.

Among British Commonwealth missiles, Canada has made one attempt to develop an air-to-air missile, the Velvet Glove, but a change in government policy called for canceling it. Australia's contributions to date are the Jindivik subsonic bomber and the huge Woomera rocket test range.

It is apparent that the British have and are achieving a great deal in all phases of missile technology. In terms of trained manpower, research and test facilities, the British Empire's potential is excellent—a potential which should someday render her one of the top three leaders in this field.

Italy

Italy, one of the pioneers in jet propulsion, has been interested in rocketry since the end of World War II. This interest has been displayed by individuals, government and industry. However, lack of funds and government direction have delayed positive action. In spite of these handicaps, however, Italy has developed several military rockets, two of which are the Airone and the Robotti. The Airone is a solid-propellant, surface-to-surface missile approximately 6 feet long and 3 inches in diameter. Range is reported to be over 6 miles. The Robotti is a surface-to-air missile propelled by a liquid rocket engine using nitric acid and aniline. It is the opinion of many rocket experts that Italy has excellent research potential and will within the next few years become a leader in the missile production field.

Japan

Japan, one of the more recent entries in the missile field, is described as one of the most enthusiastic. This country's missile activities include military rocketry, research rocketry, and spaceflight studies.

The military rockets include the MM-1 and the TMA-O-AC. The MM-1 is an air-to-air guided missile, and the TMA-O-AC is identified simply as a military rocket.

Japan's research rocket program, which is less than two years old, is the result of a decision of the National Science Council of Japan to participate in the 1957–58 International Geophysical Year (IGY). As part of this program, a decision was made to use sounding rockets to supplement balloon observations. To develop these rockets in time for the IGY, a four-year missile development program was initiated. This program called for a series of five rockets—the Pencil, Baby, Kappa, Sigma, and Omega—which would progressively lead to a very high (150-mile) IGY sounding rocket. Japan announced in October, 1957, that one of her rockets had gained a 75-mile altitude.

France

In Europe, France has been one of the leaders in the missile field since the end of World War II and has established an impressive record with her relatively limited resources. Her missile developments have been geared to the type of war she feels she is most apt to fight. In line with this philosophy, antiaircraft and wire-guided antitank missile research have been emphasized.

Some of the better known antiaircraft missiles are the Navy's Maruca and Masalca, and the Army's Sud-Est (SE) series and LRBA-DEFA's ramp-launched PARCA.

In the antitank category, the SS10 and the SS11 programs are outstanding. The first program, the SS10, includes the SFEC-MAS-5200 and DEFA's Entac missiles. These two missiles are almost identical in range and velocity. Both are wire controlled and can be launched against tanks either from the surface or from the air. The second program, the SS11, includes the SFEC-MAS-5210 missile, which is said to be a longer range version of the SFECMAS-5200.

Four other surface-to-surface missiles of importance include: (1) Zborowski's BTZ-411.01 bazooka-type, two-stage, solid-propellant missile; (2) the infantryman's Lutin, a radio-guided, rocket-boosted ramjet; (3) the Ogre I, photo-reconnaissance, liquid-propellant-boosted ramjet; and (4) the SE-4200, which is ramp launched by two solid boosters and ramjet sustained. The missile is currently in production.

There are five missiles in the air-to-air category: the M04, M20, M051, M510, and M511. Of these five, the M04 is probably the best known. The M04 can be used in either air-to-air or surface-to-air applications. It is approximately 15 feet long, 16 inches in diameter, and weighs over 1,000 pounds. This missile utilizes a liquid-propellant rocket engine, delivering 2,750 pounds of thrust for 14 seconds, and it can fly over 1,000 miles per hour, carrying approximately 245 pounds payload. The M04 was first successfully tested in 1952.

The M20 and M051 are Matra production missiles carried by the Mystere A and B fighters. The M20 uses a liquid-propellant engine, and the M051 utilizes a solid-propellant motor.

The last two missiles in this category are the M510 and M511. They are comparable in length to the Matra M051. Although the performance of these missiles is classified, it has been reported that the M511 is scheduled for use with the Trident rocket-powered airplane.

French air-to-surface missiles are the least developed and consist of only three missiles, the BB10, SNCASE1522, and an ASM, which is said to be similar to the U. S. Air Force's Rascal.

French missile designers' independent look at their missile requirements has resulted in some truly remarkable advances in the state-of-the-art. Their wire-guided antitank missiles and their antiaircraft missiles are tops in their fields. The French method of guiding antitank missiles by wire (similar to a kite) has been adopted by the United States. Also, the adaptation of ramjets in small missiles by the French has been revolutionary. France is rated as a third-ranking military power in rocket development.

Holland

A smaller nation contributing to rocketry today is Holland. Utilizing a French SFECMAS SS10 pulsejet motor, which develops 190 pounds thrust, the Aviolanda Company developed a pilotless target aircraft. The plane is boost launched by rockets, has a conventional aircraft configuration, and is radio controlled.

Soviet Union

The Soviet Union, one of the two giants in the guided-missile field today, achieved its missile mastery within a record-breaking period from an incredibly primitive start. It is fairly obvious from present results that the Russians, after taking over Peenemünde and enlisting the aid of many of its former specialists, made exceptionally good use of both.

Although many, if not most, of her current missiles reflect the design and thinking of the German influence, Russia today is completely on her own. The transition from almost complete dependence on German know-how to complete independence took place essentially within three five-year periods.

The first period, from 1945 to 1950, was one in which the Russian missile industry depended a hundred percent on the experience of the German rocket specialists in all branches. This was the Russian learning period. It is reported that from the beginning the Russians followed a policy of picking clean the Nazi rocket scientists' brains. Soviet scientists and engineers observed every move the Germans made and quizzed them endlessly on the Peenemünde experiments and general German rocket theory.

In the second period, from 1950–55, Russian specialists began to phase out their German counterparts. And finally, in the third period, i.e., since 1955, the Russian missile industry has been entirely on its own and is making tremendous headway.

Today, the Russian arsenal not only includes special application missiles, such as their satellite-launching and high-altitude research vehicles, but also has missiles in all four major military categories: air-to-air, air-to-surface, surface-to-air, and surface-to-surface. The last category, surface-to-surface, includes the particularly important submarine underwater-launched missile.

In the air-to-air category the Russians basically have two missiles, the 3.2-inch rocket and M-100 series. The 3.2-inch rocket is the standard missile in this category. It is said that the 3.2 is a carryover from the German World War II, R4M, which was a spin-stabilized, short-range, solid-propellant missile.

The M-100 and M-100A are higher performing rockets from the same family. The M-100A is approximately 8 feet long and 10 inches in diameter, and weighs between 100 to 200 pounds. It is a production missile propelled by a solid-propellant motor with a range of about 5 miles.

There are reported to be four missiles in the air-to-surface group: the RS82, RS132, RS-URS-132, and the Comet III. The first three of this grouping are unguided solid-propellant missiles, and the Comet III, which is radar guided, has a range of approximately 100 miles.

The surface-to-air category lists three missiles: the M-1, T-7, and the T-8. The first vehicle, the M-1, is 14.7 feet long, 22 inches in diameter, and has a takeoff gross weight of 3,300 pounds. It is solid-boost launched, sustained by a hydrogen peroxide and hydrazine liquid-propellant engine, and has a maximum operational ceiling of about 50,000 feet. The performance of this missile is somewhat comparable to the U. S. Army's Nike. Although the M-1 is now obsolete, it initially was pressed into service several years ago as a defense against the U. S. Air Force's B-29 and B-36 bombers.

The second missile in this category, the T-7, is a more efficient performing missile based on the German World War II, Wasserfall. The T-7 is 25 feet long and 25 inches in diameter. It weighs 3 to 4 tons and has a maximum altitude of 75,000 feet. Like the M-1, it is boost launched and sustained by a liquid-propellant engine. The missile was designed to defend Russian targets against potential attacks from B-47 and B-52 bombers. United States authorities have confirmed that these missiles are currently in production and are located at missile sites around most major target areas.

The last vehicle in the surface-to-air group is the T-8, which is employed as a barrage flak weapon against low-altitude targets.

In the surface-to-surface type can be found the heart of the Russian military and scientific missile strength. As such, this list includes the medium range ballistic missiles, intermediate range missiles, intercontinental ballistic missiles, as well as the satellite-launching and lunar vehicles. Each of the missiles in this

family is of extreme importance, and therefore will be discussed
in some detail in the order mentioned above.

There are three missiles in the medium-range, surface-to-surface category. These missiles are the T-1 (M-101), the S8 and
the T-7A. The T-1 is said to be an improved version of the
German V-2. It is estimated to be 50 feet long, 5.5 feet in diameter and powered by a liquid oxygen and kerosene rocket engine.
The engine thrust is rated at 77,000 pounds, and the range is
given as 400 miles. The S8 is said to be another modification of
the German V-2, and is somewhat similar to the T-1. This
vehicle is specifically designed to be launched from underground
tubes. The last missile of the medium-range, surface-to-surface
type is the T-7A. This vehicle is 25 feet long, has a diameter of
2.5 feet, and a takeoff gross weight of 8,800 pounds. It is reported that the vehicle is currently in production and is operational.

The Russians have four missiles in their arsenal in the inter-
mediate range, surface-to-surface classification. Two of these, the
T-2 (M-103) and T-4 (M-102) belong to the Army, and Comets
I and II are Soviet Navy missiles.

The Army's T-2 is an improved version of the German two-
stage A-4/A-9, which was initially designed by the Germans to
bomb New York during World War II. The T-2 is approximately
125 feet in length, 15 feet in diameter and has a range of 1,800
miles. The first-stage propulsion system is a liquid-propellant
rocket engine utilizing liquid oxygen and kerosene as propellants. The engine thrust is rated at approximately 254,000
pounds. It should be noted that the second stage of the T-2 is
basically the T-1 (engine thrust 77,000 pounds).

The second of the Army's intermediate range vehicles is the
T-4. The T-4 is still another version of the German V-2, differ-
ing only by the addition of wings. This vehicle is a production
item and is commonly known as the winged T-1. It has the same
engine as the T-1 and a reported maximum range of 1,000 miles.
This missile is also recognized as a test bed for the T-4A, hypersonic glide bomber.

In order to evaluate fully and accurately the Russian missile capability, the Soviet naval missile arsenal must be taken into consideration. It is most generally known that the Soviet Navy is well equipped for missile warfare. Its submarine fleet is said to number between 400 to 800 operational vessels with an additional 100 under construction. In addition to the vast submarine fleet, the Soviet Navy is being equipped with several types of missile ships; for example, antiaircraft and short and medium range missile attack ships. United States Naval Intelligence has admitted that the Soviet Navy is second only to the United States Fleet in numbers and is growing very fast.

Probably one of the most potentially dangerous weapons systems that the Russians can deploy against the United States and the Free World is their growing submarine fleet, coupled with their underwater-launched ballistic missiles. Of the several techniques available for launching missiles underwater, in all probability a modified version of the deadly German V-2 submersible ballistic missile launcher would be used. In the older German plan, three V-2 missiles in their containers could be towed horizontally and underwater by one submarine at approximately fifteen miles per hour from German seaports to any coastline, depending only on the cruise capacity of the submarine. Once on location, and to ready the missile for launching, the ballast end of the container was to be flooded, forcing the container into the vertical position. When in the upright position, a built-in gyroscope system would hold the container in the desired launch position by counteracting any yaw or roll movements. The missile container was to be outfitted with a control station and propellant tankage in addition to the necessary servicing equipment. The weight of the container and missile was about 70 tons of which the missile and propellants represented about 35 tons. After the necessary prelaunch servicing, the missile was to be remotely fired from the mother submarine.

When the Russians took Peenemünde, they acquired this fantastic weapons system which was then ready for production!

It is no secret that the Russian Navy is today capable of towing huge ballistic rockets in their submersible containers to any coastline that it desires. With only part of its fleet of 800 sub-

marines assigned to such a mission, it could position offshore in
close proximity to any target within the United States. Furthermore, a mission of this type does not require ICBM's nor necessarily IRBM's. Most target areas could probably be reached with
the Soviet Navy's Comet I and Comet II missiles reputed to
have a range of 100 and 700 miles respectively.

Dr. Walter Dornberger, former Peenemünde Commandant,
has said he believes the Russian "emphasis on underwater vessels
indicates a plan to use submarines offensively, in American
waters, quite possibly as two vessels for missile launchers."

Completing the military arsenal are Russia's ICBM and antipodal bomber programs. The Russian ICBM designated as the
T-3 (M-104) is reported to be a two-stage vehicle approximately
100 to 160 feet in length, and 100 to 150 tons in weight. The
first stage is said to be powered by two T-2 motors (254,000
pounds of thrust each), and the second stage by a single T-1
motor (77,000 pounds of thrust). The hypersonic antipodal
(skip-glide) bomber has been reported in a number of journals as
weighing 100 tons, with the boost stage engines delivering between 800,000 and 1,000,000 pounds thrust and having an attack capability at approximately 10,000 miles per hour.

The last family of vehicles in the surface-to-surface category
and certainly one of the most interesting is the scientific research
vehicle. Two vehicles of particular current interest are the satellite-launching vehicle and the lunar vehicle.

Since the Russians launched their first Earth satellite, they
have not as yet officially released information regarding the
satellite-launching vehicle. This silence on the part of the Russian scientists and engineers has resulted in many irresponsible
press releases from responsible quarters in the United States regarding the Soviet capability. However, cooler heads have pre-
vailed, and, today, there seems to be a consensus of opinion
regarding this vehicle's configuration as well as the overall Russian missile capability.

It is most generally agreed that the Russian satellite-launching vehicle is basically a modification of the T-3 intercontinental
ballistic missile, and that it was assembled adapting existing

hardware such as the T-1 and Wasserfall engines. The vehicle is described as being approximately 100 feet long, 7 to 8 feet in diameter and having a takeoff gross weight of 150,000 pounds. It is a three-stage vehicle using the same propellants in all stages, namely, liquid oxygen and kerosene. The first-stage propulsion system is the 254,000-pound-thrust T-2 engine; the second stage is the T-1, 77,000-pound-thrust engine; and the third stage is said to be a 20,000-pound-thrust improved Wasserfall engine.

Switzerland

Another nation which has been actively engaged in missile production is Switzerland. The Orelikon Company has developed missiles in all but one of the four major military categories.

The surface-to-air (antiaircraft) development of the "Series 50" missiles started shortly after World War II. They weigh about 550 pounds each and have a range and ceiling of 12 miles. The more recent "Series 54" has a takeoff gross weight of 772 pounds. It is powered by a nitric acid-hydrocarbon fuel, liquid rocket engine delivering about 2,200 pounds thrust. The range and ceiling are 15.5 miles and 9.3 miles respectively. The "Series 56" and "Series 57" are the latest versions under development.

In the air-to-surface category, Orelikon has produced two outstanding FF, FF (forward-firing, folding-fin) missiles. These two missiles have been developed expressly for the British Gloster Meteor and Venom aircraft. The Cobra, another Orelikon missile, is a surface-to-surface, wire-controlled, solid-propellant, antitank missile. The weight of the Cobra is reported to be one-tenth the weight of the U. S. Army's Dart.

The most significant aspect of the Orelikon Company's operations is its policy of selling missiles to any foreign power throughout the world.

Sweden

Sweden, another small nation engaged in missile activities, has one of the better rounded programs. In addition to her missile activity, she is actively engaged in research on high-energy fuels, ramjet propulsion, and advanced rocket designs. Specifically, Sweden's missile program has one missile in three of the four basic military categories. These include the Jaktrobot, an air-to-air in development; the Sjorobot, a surface-to-surface naval missile soon to become operational; and the Luftforsvarsrobot, a surface-to-air missile in development for her Air Force since 1955. This missile is said to be capable of interception at very high altitudes and at extreme ranges (120 to 150 miles).

United States

The United States missile program after World War II was one which emphasized the "broad look" into the state-of-the-art and not quantity production of systems with questionable tactical value. Whereas, the Soviets adopted postwar crash programs which utilized German rocketry knowledge both for immediate production and as a point of departure for building systems that could span continents.

It was intended that the policy of the United States should eventually result in the development and production of a select few missiles which would be the best available in their respective categories. It was also intended that this period, like the Russian five-year "brain picking" period, should fill many of the basic research and engineering gaps as well as build up a cadre of missile specialists throughout the supporting industries.

This concept, coupled with the pressures of an uncertain international picture, was indirectly responsible for fostering the much-discussed parallel programming of the missile efforts which is still in existence today (Jupiter-Thor). Although the international pressures during the immediate postwar period were not as acute (because of the then nuclear superiority in the United States) as they are today, they were, nevertheless, present.

These pressures even in the postwar period did not permit a normal, step-by-step engineering approach. Instead they dictated the simultaneous support of several approaches to the same problem in the hope that one would pay off. It was recognized that each branch of the military service had special tactical obligations possibly requiring missiles in the same category, and, furthermore, that these requirements would naturally lead to competition and probably duplication in some areas. Moreover, as the state-of-the-art developed, a more critical evaluation of these projects was possible. These evaluations resulted in canceling less promising projects (Navaho) and placing greater emphasis on the more promising ones (Atlas and Titan).

As to the soundness of this philosophy, there is agreement among those close to the facts that this concept has permitted the investigation of a greater number of approaches to a particular missile problem; that this policy has also resulted in producing in a shorter period of time greater quantities of technical information, which was readily exchanged between projects, allowing one group to profit from the experience of the other; and that in the final analysis it has developed the potential for producing far-better weapons systems in the future.

Perhaps the most significant event after World War II which gave the greatest impetus to American rocketry was the shipment of stocks of unused German V-2's for upper air research and operational training purposes. The highlight of this program came in 1946 when a two-stage vehicle consisting of a WAC Corporal atop a V-2 reached a record altitude of 244 miles and a speed of 5,000 miles per hour.

To supplement the depleted V-2 stockpiles in the latter part of the 1940's, limited funds were granted for building bigger and better research rockets. The Aerobee and the Martin Viking were developed at this time. Viking 11 still holds the world's altitude record for a single-stage rocket (158.4 miles).

With the advent of war in Korea, missile development programs were given new impetus. This acceleration was reflected in the missile budget. In the fiscal year, 1951, the missile budget was $21,000,000; in 1952, it was increased to $169,000,000; and in 1953, it reached $800,000,000. The one billion mark was surpassed in 1954; and, in late 1957, it went over the two-billion-dollars-a-year level and is still increasing.

Thus, within the last ten years, the United States missile industry has grown from the precarious incubator stage to a healthy three-billion-dollars-a-year business and is still expanding in all directions.

There are today in the United States approximately 1,000 industries engaged in development, research, or production of rockets and missiles. To some, rocketry represents 100 percent of their business; furthermore, these industries employ about 50,000 engineers and technical specialists, as well as an estimated 100,000 other employees on the nontechnical level. The three branches of the Armed Forces have also committed a significant percentage of their manpower (in addition to their utilization of more than half of the nation's civilian scientific manpower), to implement their respective missile defense responsibilities.

Since the early V-2 experiments, the nation has developed and produced successful missiles in all four major military categories. The giants in the surface-to-surface category are nearing an advanced stage of development, and by the end of 1958 the United States probably will have successfully launched several artificial Earth satellites.

Without question, rocketry in the United States today is in a crucial transitional period where momentary daily developments can alter significantly the scientific, political, and military status of the nation. To appreciate its current missile position, let us examine in greater detail some of the most important missiles in the basic tactical and strategic categories, considering first the air-to-air family.

There are presently four major missiles in the air-to-air category, namely the Mighty Mouse, Falcon, Sparrow I, and the Sidewinder. Of these four, the Mighty Mouse is the oldest and best known. It has been the most reliable and for years the most utilized of its category. The Mighty Mouse is 48 inches long, 2.75 inches in diameter, and is propelled by a solid rocket motor. The projectile is equipped with a homing head and a proximity fuse. The power of the Air Force's Mighty Mouse is equivalent to a 70-mm. cannon shell which probably is sufficient to bring down the largest aircraft.

One of the newer guided types of Air Force air-to-air missiles is the Falcon. The Falcon is slightly less than 78 inches in length and has a span of 20 inches. It is powered by a solid-propellant motor with 6,000 pounds thrust, has a range of about 5 miles and a top velocity better than 1,200 miles per hour. The missile is radar guided, and its kill rate is high. This missile has the lethal power to stop any aircraft.

Two of the newer missiles in this category are the Navy's Sparrow I and the Sidewinder. The Sparrow, now operational in the fleet, is powered by a solid motor and is radar guided. The accuracy of this missile has been demonstrated against other aircraft and missiles. There are currently two other versions of the Sparrow, the Sparrow II and the Sparrow III. It has been reported that the Sparrow II will replace the Canadian Velvet Glove.

The Sidewinder is another naval air operational missile. It is 9 feet long and 4½ inches in diameter. The powerplant is a solid-propellant motor. Guidance is infrared homing. The range is approximately five miles and currently the kill rate is said to be seven out of ten. It is reported that the Navy intends to replace the Sparrow I with the Sidewinder.

There are three other missiles in this category that should be mentioned. The first is the Ding-Dong, a liquid-propelled missile capable of carrying atomic warheads. Little is known of this missile, but it is said to be in the advanced stages of development. The second is the Diamondback. The performance of this missile is not known. Finally, the third is the Navy's Zuni. The Zuni is an air-to-air or an air-to-ground missile. It can be used in conjunction with high performance fighters and attack-type aircraft. It can be used against other aircraft as well as against such ground targets as tanks, gun implacements, etc.

In the air-to-surface category the Navy seems to be particularly active, especially in antisubmarine applications. In the past decade the Navy has had more than six missiles in this family, although it is not known whether any are currently operational. The Tiny Tim is the best known of this category. Since the Tiny Tim, there have been the Petrel, Dove, Goose, and the Duck.

More recently, the Navy has been evaluating the Bullpup,

also an air-to-ground missile. It is expected that this missile will soon join the fleet. The missile is approximately 11 feet long and a foot in diameter. It is powered by a solid-propellant motor. The Bulldog, a larger improved version of the Bullpup, is also a solid-propellant missile in this class.

Finally, one of the newer Navy air-to-surface missiles is the Corvus, designed for use on carrier-based aircraft. Its current status is unknown; however, it is known that the missile's aero-dynamic characteristics have been evaluated through wind tunnel tests.

As far as the Air Force is concerned, they have only one missile in the air-to-surface class, the Rascal. The Rascal is approximately 35 feet long and 4½ feet in diameter. It is powered by three 6,000-pound-thrust engines, has a speed of approximately 1,000 miles per hour and a range of 100 miles. There is no additional information available on its current status.

There are currently six missiles in the antiaircraft category. They are as follows: the Nike Ajax, the Nike Hercules, the Hawk, the Terrier, the Tartar, and the Talos. The primary function of the ground-to-air missile is the protection of major cities, vital industries, and ships at sea from every type of enemy aircraft carrying modern warheads or guided missiles. In addition, this weapons system must be capable of stopping multiple threats from several directions and altitudes simultaneously and at safe distances consistent with the types of warheads employed.

The best known of our antiaircraft missiles are the Nike Ajax and the Nike Hercules.

The Nike Ajax is approximately 20 feet long and a foot in diameter. Speed is 1,500 miles per hour, range 10 to 30 miles, and ceiling about 50,000 feet. The vehicle is solid rocket boost launched and has a liquid rocket sustainer. The Nike Ajax is now in service, being mass produced, and delivered to antiaircraft batteries in and around major cities and vital industrial areas throughout the United States. Each Nike battery consists of 12 missile launchers, manned and operated by approximately 100 officers and enlisted men. Although the Nike is designed to intercept moving and evasive targets and has an exceptional kill potential, it has been the subject of controversy. It has been argued that the missile does not offer sufficient down-range protection against high-flying modern aircraft carrying nuclear or H-bomb warheads.

The second of the Nike series, the Nike Hercules, has been developed as a replacement for the Ajax and has been called the "double" Ajax. The Hercules is 27 feet long and 2 feet in diameter. The vehicle is solid-boost launched and solid rocket motor sustained; the speed is 2,000 to 2,300 miles per hour; and range is reported as three times the range of the Ajax, or about 70 miles. The missile is described as being far more maneuverable and deadly than the Ajax because of its atomic warhead. The Hercules is currently in the final stages of development and initial stages of production. Replacement of the Ajax by the Hercules should begin in spring, 1958.

The Army's Hawk was designed to supplement the Nike; i.e., fill the gap between zero altitude and minimum Nike altitude capability. The Hawk is 16 feet, 4 inches long and 14 inches in diameter. It is propelled by a solid rocket motor. The speed has been described as being highly supersonic with a range of 50 miles. The missile is in the final stages of development, and, when it is made available, it most likely will first see service in the New York City and the Washington-Baltimore areas.

The Terrier, a Navy missile, is in operational use on the cruisers U.S.S. *Boston*, U.S.S. *Canberra* and the destroyer U.S.S. *Gyatt*. The missile is 27 feet long and a foot in diameter. Speed is 1,500 miles per hour, range about 20 miles, and ceiling 60,000 feet. The missile is boost launched and sustained by a solid rocket motor. By 1961, Terrier I is expected to be operational on approximately 22 capital ships. Terrier II, currently under development, is reported to be twice the size of Terrier I.

The Tartar, another Navy missile from this category, is a substantially more efficient single-stage vehicle that is expected to replace Terrier I by 1961. This missile, currently in the early production phases, will be used as secondary batteries on large ships or destroyers, and on other small vessels.

At the present time the arsenal of short-range, surface-to-surface tactical missiles consists of four members: Honest John, Little John, Dart, and the LaCrosse. The function of these short-range, surface-to-surface missiles is twofold. First, it must provide the infantryman with an effective weapons system for defending himself against all immediate fixed and mobile units; and, secondly, it must have the capability of reaching behind the immediate contact area to destroy select targets.

Probably the best known of this family is the Honest John. The Honest John is 27 feet long and 2.5 feet in diameter. The range of this weapon has been quoted as 20 to 30 miles. The vehicle is powered by a solid rocket motor and is an unguided, free-flight artillery rocket capable of delivering nuclear warheads. It is currently assigned to the Army's new pentomic divisions. The first tactical unit armed with this rocket was the 101st Airborne Division.

The Little John is, as the name implies, a smaller solid rocket motor missile with a shorter range. It was designed to supplement the Honest John and provide all-weather artillery support.

The Dart is one of the newest missiles that has been developed. It is 5 feet long, 8 inches in diameter and has a 3-foot wing span. Speed is over 600 miles per hour. The range is unknown, although in one public demonstration the missile hit the target at a range of 2,100 yards. The Dart is powered by a single-stage smokeless solid rocket motor and is wire guided. Since its range exceeds that of any known tank armament, it can be fired safely from a fixed or mobile position. The missile is in production but is not yet operational.

The LaCrosse is a solid rocket motor propelled, all-weather, ground-support missile developed for the Army and the Marine Corps.

It is 20 feet long, 20.5 inches in diameter, and has a range of 15 to 20 miles. The missile is truck mounted and extremely mobile. It is currently in production.

With these four new missiles—Honest John, Little John, Dart, and LaCrosse—supplementing weapons in this category that have been battle proved in the last two wars, the American infantryman is assured of the close support required.

In the medium-range, surface-to-surface category (enemy ground targets up to 500 miles), there are the Corporal (the most popularly known of this group), the Sergeant, and the Jupiter A (Redstone) missiles.

The Corporal is approximately 45 feet long and 2.5 feet in diameter. It weighs about 5 tons fully fueled, and the range is about 150 miles. This vehicle is one of the nation's first guided missiles. It is radio guided, flies a ballistic trajectory after cutoff, and can carry an atomic warhead. The missile is currently in large-scale production and in full use by the Armed Forces.

The Sergeant missile, an outgrowth of the Hermes RVA-10, is a late addition to the Army's tactical missile family. It is more than 22 feet long and 3 feet in diameter. With a launch weight of 25,000 to 35,000 pounds including the payload, the range of this missile is estimated at 50 to 70 miles. Thrust is estimated at 50,000 to 75,000 pounds. The propulsion system is said to be one of the largest solid-propellant motors in development. When this vehicle becomes operational, it may replace the Corporal.

The last vehicle in this series is the Jupiter A, more commonly known as Redstone. It is 69 feet long and 6 feet in diameter. The range of the vehicle is given as 200 to 250 miles. The Jupiter A resembles the V-2 in many respects and is described as the test bed for the Jupiter C, in addition to its tactical function. The vehicle is powered by a 75,000-pound-thrust, liquid-propellant engine. This particular powerplant, although not as efficient as the more modern engines, is nevertheless one of the more reliable. It is expected that the Jupiter A will become operational shortly. When it does, the utilization of this weapon will extend the Army's striking capability well beyond the Army group zone of action.

As of January 1, 1958, the United States had under development five long-range ballistic missiles. Basically they are of two types: the shorter range 1,500-mile intermediate range ballistic missile (IRBM); and the extreme range 500- to 5,500-mile intercontinental ballistic missile (ICBM). Of the five missiles under development, three are in the shorter intermediate range, and the other two are in the intercontinental range.

In the IRBM class, the Thor is being developed by the Air Force, the Jupiter by the Army, and the Polaris, by the Navy.

The Thor, officially designated as the WS-315, is a single-stage missile powered by a liquid rocket engine of 135,000 pounds thrust. It is claimed that the development of the Thor will serve as a component test bed for the Atlas and Titan ICBM's. The Thor is currently undergoing development testing. The first three firings of this missile ended in failures; however, the ultimate success of this weapon is not questioned. When it is released for operational use, the Strategic Air Command will be responsible for its tactical deployment.

The Jupiter, like the Thor, is a single-stage, intermediate range ballistic missile. The similarities do not end here. Both vehicles use the same engine, and it has been reported that they may also adapt the same airframes. This vehicle is estimated to be 50 to 60 feet in length and 8 feet in diameter. The Jupiter IRBM, like the Thor, has known test failures. The first two failures of the Jupiter test vehicle were attributed to sloshing fuel. The third test vehicle was a success and flew its prescribed range of 1,500 miles. The Navy had initially sponsored the development of the Jupiter with the Army, but, because of special shipboard problems, the Polaris was substituted for the Jupiter by the Navy.

The Polaris is a two-stage, fleet ballistic missile vehicle capable of being launched from surface ships or from underwater by special submarines. The propulsion system is a solid rocket motor, said to be the largest built to date. The motor is housed within a vehicle approximately 40 to 50 feet long and 100 inches in diameter. Range is given as 800 to 1,500 miles, and the warhead is said to be nuclear.

It is the opinion of the authors that the sublaunch IRBM will achieve a role of greater strategic significance in the very near future. Furthermore, it is believed that the use of the solid-propellant motor for this application will come of age and be accepted by all services. (It is interesting to note that there is no evidence to date that the Soviets have developed a large solid motor for extreme-range missiles.)

The United States Air Force has the prime responsibility for developing the ICBM. There are two missiles that are currently under development in this category—the Atlas and the Titan.

The Atlas is approximately 100 feet in length and 12 feet in diameter. The vehicle is boosted by two 135,000-pound-thrust, liquid-propellant engines and sustained by a single 100,000-pound-thrust, liquid-propellant engine. The Atlas is known as a "stage and a half missile," i.e., "parallel staged," somewhat similar to the British wrap-around technique. At launch all three engines are utilized. The vehicle takeoff gross weight is over 200,000 pounds. Its maximum range is 5,500 miles, apogee (maximum altitude) about 800 miles and re-entry velocity approximately 15,000 miles per hour. The expected accuracy is 20 miles, using celestial guidance. The current status or operational date of the missile is not known, but it is expected to be sometime after 1960. The first two firings of this vehicle in June and September, 1957, ended in misfire. The cause has been traced to failure in the propellant feed system. Finally, on December 17, 1957, the third Atlas test vehicle was successfully launched and guided several hundred miles down range to a prescribed target area.

The Titan, currently a backup to the Atlas project, is a more sophisticated approach to the ICBM design. The Titan is a two-stage "tandem" vehicle with an estimated length of over 100 feet and diameter of 10 feet. The vehicle weighs more than 200,000 pounds at takeoff. The propulsion system is believed to have 300,000 pounds of thrust in the first stage and 60,000 pounds of thrust in the second. The missile is currently in the development phase—and Air Force officials have said that they are pleased with the progress.

The missile arsenal would be incomplete without mention of the surface-to-surface, air-breathing, pilotless aircraft missiles.

Currently, there are four surface-to-surface pilotless aircraft. There are the Navy's Triton and Regulus II and the Air Force's Snark and Matador. The propulsion for these vehicles is either

Plate 3—First unmanned lunar landing will consist of three vehicles —two drones and one instrument probe. The drones will explode on impact, covering a large area with dye markers. The instrumented probe in the upper left will relay messages back to Earth after landing in the dye-marked area.

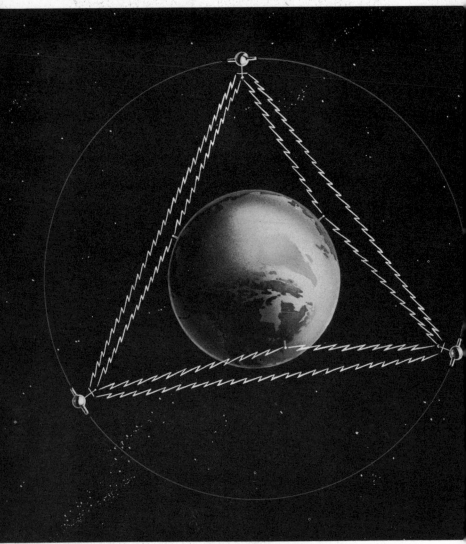

Fig. 4—The improvement of mass communication on a global scale (TV, telephone, and radio) with the aid of high-altitude satellites.

turbojet or ramjet, and the ranges vary from the Matador's medium range of 600 miles to the Triton and Regulus with a range from 1,000 to 1,500 miles. The Snark can claim a range of over 5,000 miles. All vehicles are capable of carrying nuclear warheads. The prime difference between these vehicles is that the Navy vehicles are launched from submarines; whereas, the Air Force vehicles are launched conventionally.

The antiaircraft, air-breathing missiles are the well-known Navy Talos and the Air Force Bomarc. As is characteristic with all air-breathing engines, there are operational limits in both speed and altitude.

The Air Force's Bomarc, because of its long-range capabilities is known as an "area" antiaircraft defense missile, as opposed to the Army's Nike "point defense" missile. The Bomarc is almost 47 feet long and 3 feet in diameter. Speeds and altitudes have not been officially released; however, some of the earlier test vehicles achieved velocities of over 1,500 miles and altitudes of over 60,000 feet. The range is given as 200 to 300 miles. The vehicle is boosted by a liquid rocket and sustained by two ramjet engines. The range of the missile is greater than the other missiles of this category. On May 16, 1957, the Bomarc was awarded an initial production contract. It is expected that as soon as the Bomarc becomes available in quantity, it will be operated by the Air Defense Command in the more strategic areas.

We have summarized the state of missile development today among nations. It must be noted that we have only touched on the highlights and that most nations have missiles other than those mentioned, either developed or being developed, including rocket-powered aircraft.

Criteria to Gauge a Nation's Missile Potential

A look at the missile arsenal in any nation is only one factor in the evaluation of its missile potential. In addition to missile hardware, a comprehensive evaluation should include the following equally pertinent factors:

1. A nation's potential in the missile field should be measured by the current caliber of its leaders and numbers of scientists, engineers, and trained technicians, as well as by the capability of its educational institutions to train and maintain the balance of technical and nontechnical personnel required for the future.

2. A nation's potential in the missile field should also be measured by its natural resources, by the numbers of its supporting industries, and by the quality of its basic research and test facilities.

3. And, furthermore, a nation's potential in the missile field should be measured by the availability of operational missiles in any one of the four basic military categories, which fulfill that nation's specific strategic requirements.

Eight Axioms on Missilery

In addition to the above criteria for gauging a nation's missile potential, we offer the following eight axioms on missilery as a means for a realistic assessment of rocketry today:

1. The statement "behind in the missile race" without qualification is meaningless.

2. If leads in certain missile categories do exist, it is primarily because of a concentrated effort in that area.

3. Rocketry is a matter of emphasis—not just on funding but also in direction.

4. The know-how of building missiles and rockets is not one nation's secret, nor is this know-how limited to a select few organizations or scientists. The physics of rocketry is well understood by many both here and abroad.

5. At present it appears that no nation has made a major missile technological breakthrough. This is especially true from an aerodynamic and propulsion viewpoint.

6. The probability of a successful missile launching applies "equally" to all nations.

7. The citizens of the United States and the leaders they have

elected over at least the last fifteen years are responsible for the nation's current position in rocketry.

8. An informed people will ensure that American democracy will courageously and successfully meet the challenge of the coming Space Age.

chapter 4

boosters anonymous

It seems logical that the Air Force, when the ICBM's become operational, will want to train their launching crews
and test their vehicles under realistic conditions—and a
good way to do it might well be to send modified versions of these vehicles into orbits around the moon.

Brig. Gen. Hollingsworth F. Gregory
Commander, Air Force Office of Scientific Research
U. S. Air Force
Missiles and Rockets—March, 1957

AFTER each of the leading nations of the world
catch up with one another in the current missiles race, there
should come a period of the lowering of the pressure in the global
political boiler, that may even usher in an era of relative tran-
quillity for a spell. This period will arise when the world finds
itself in the manmade dilemma of having thousands of complex
and expensive "operational" ballistic missiles protruding from
myriad spots on its surface and subsurface like porcupine quills.

When this situation develops, as assuredly it must, the United
States will find itself in an embarrassing dilemma that will have
many facets and multitudinous solutions. Will the nation's economy be disrupted again as it was after World War II, by the
dropping of outstanding missile defense contracts and by laying
off thousands of trained scientists and missile technicians and
forcing them to seek employment elsewhere and in other nontechnical fields? The basic problem, though, will boil itself down
to the question of the uses of the large ballistic rocket boosters.

For what purposes will they be employed? Offensive? Defensive? Or peaceful? Once the United States realizes that it can choose from among these three broad goals, then it can face up to the reality of the practical alternatives for the utilization of rocket boosters in the future.

The leading nations of the world will then face four possible significant alternatives when they find themselves possessing sufficient quantities of expensive long-range missiles and rockets in their respective arsenals. They can either: (1) use them in an all-out quick war of annihilation of civilization as we know it; or (2) keep them poised "on the ready" at their operational complexes (this state can only be for a limited time because of the perishable nature of complex rockets); or (3) allow them to rust and mildew "on the shelf"; or (4) put them to use as vehicles to conduct scientific tests.

There is a strong possibility that the nonmilitary uses of large rocket boosters will eventually be the path chosen by the leading nations of the world.

Large-scale boosters built for scientific purposes can do much to maintain a necessary industrial balance when nations are "full up" on defensive requirements.

Additional arguments to utilize ICBM's and IRBM's for the last alternative—peaceful scientific purposes—can be inferred after reading Henry Kissinger's recent provocative book, *Nuclear Weapons and Foreign Policy*. This best-selling book has stirred official Washington more than any other tome in recent years. The author propounds the thesis that small nuclear wars are both possible and probable. With both the United States and the Soviet Union possessing long-range bombers carrying nuclear weapons and now ICBM's, the chance of total global annihilation appears dim to Kissinger, *if* both the nations keep their powder dry.

He argues cogently for the United States to have both the means and the will to fight small "brush fire" wars that might arise along the lines of the recent Near East affair. If his thesis becomes the pattern of events in the near future, then we might theoretically and realistically find ourselves with a "surplus" of operational ICBM's and IRBM's on hand. These longer range weapons would be "deteriorating" at their secret launching sites, while shorter range tactical missiles would be those which would be put to actual military use.

Today in the Libyan desert, tactical short-range missile crews of the U. S. Air Force keep in practice by frequent firings of 600-mile, subsonic Matadors across the desert wastes, without endangering any lives. But ICBM crews, practicing with their 5,000-mile, 15,000-m.p.h. Goliaths, have a problem, since very few spots on this Earth afford them the opportunity of testing the full length of the long-range missile trajectory without endangering lives.

To ascertain possible peaceful scientific uses of ICBM's, we shall first look at announced Soviet plans and then analyze stated and potential American plans to modify these complex vehicles to achieve these ends.

Possible Scientific Uses of Soviet Long-Range Missiles

The T-3 ICBM as a Satellite Launcher

From a late June, 1957, Moscow press "leak" came news of the first use contemplated by the Soviets for their T-3 ICBM. They announced that this vehicle was a potential carrier of the first Russian Earth satellite during the IGY. Although predictions were being bandied about in certain authoritative quarters in the West that the Soviets would be able to launch a successful Earth satellite by mid-September, the expected event finally came to pass on October 4.

The Soviets, by modifying several of their T-3 ICBM prototypes, were able to beat the West by launching the first successful Earth satellite. Using Soviet long-range missiles as satellite carriers is to date the first example of using these vehicles to help advance man's knowledge of his environs.

Other Soviet Hints for Scientific Uses of Large Rockets

Professor G. A. Chebotarev, of the Russian Academy of Sciences Institute of Theoretical Astronomy, made the following observations recently in a leading Soviet journal: "Once the artificial satellites are created, the next step in the conquest of cosmic space will be to send 'automatic rockets' to the moon and the nearest planets of the solar system and to guide them back to earth. . . ."

He went on to say that with a "large" rocket it is possible to make observations of the far side of the Moon. His prediction on the length of the flight to the Moon and back . . . was ten days.

Soviet Moon Rockets

At the Eighth Annual Congress of the International Astronautical Federation in Barcelona, Spain, during October, 1957, Dr. Leonid Sedov, the head of the Soviet delegation, and his cohorts, in conversations with American delegates, revealed some facts about their Moon rocket programs:

1. Their first Moon rocket (probably using one of their F-4 rocket engines with 820,000 pounds thrust) might carry a payload as large as 1,500 to 2,000 pounds to either hit the Moon or circumnavigate our natural satellite.

2. A second type of lunar vehicle will be designed to retard its fall toward the Moon with reverse thrust rockets so that the vehicle would be able to land its transmitter intact on the Moon's surface.

3. The third type of Moon rocket will carry television cameras to relay closeups of the Moon's craters back to Earth.

4. The fourth type will probably carry animals or even a man —if the previous attempts listed above have been successful, and if the instrumentation data has been encouraging enough to risk manned round-trip flights to the Moon and back.

When asked if he thought it was possible to establish a manned observation post on the Moon in this century, Dr. Sedov replied:

"Of course; at the rate we are progressing now, it shouldn't take too long."

There is a good possibility that the Soviets will start conducting these aforementioned scientific tests without permission of any international body—once the International Geophysical Year is ended on December 31, 1958, and the Soviet Union is no longer bound by the IGY protocol. With allocations of long-range missiles from the Soviet Army after the IGY moves on into history, Russia could prolong her intensive study of the Earth on her own terms.

Scientific Uses for American Long-Range Missiles

The glamour and limelight in the United States have been focused on the Vanguard Earth satellite rocket. This sophisticated 72-foot, three-stage vehicle, consisting of the basic three types of propulsion systems, caught the fancy of most Americans. This rocket and the Army's Jupiter C—a modified Redstone with clusters of solid-propellant rockets on top—were the leading candidates as entries of the United States into the scientific IGY satellite derby. The Vanguard was the first finless rocket to use gimbaled (swivel-mounted) engines for pitch and yaw control.

These satellite-launching rockets, which were designed to eject small satellites into orbits at 300 miles altitude, were planned to transmit valuable scientific data.

By now, several American satellites are orbiting and sending back experimental data to their minitrack and Moonwatch receiving stations situated all over the Earth. The Jupiter C rocket had the honor of boosting the first American (18-pound) satellite into an orbit around the Earth on January 31, 1958. These two rockets (Jupiter and Vanguard) are symbols of the first steps in using large rockets for peaceful, scientific purposes.

Enormous gains for scientists everywhere may be realized when successful peaceful test shots of larger vehicles, such as ICBM's, are directed into outer space. An exact measurement of the velocity of light, which has stumped scientific minds to date, would be another possible use of this device.

In addition to more knowledge about the nature of light, including the Earth's albedo (earth glow from reflected sunlight), other experiments can be undertaken that can help both Earth scientists and Air Force medical scientists probing the human survival factors in outer space.

Brigadier General Hollingsworth F. Gregory, of the Air Force Office of Scientific Research, has stated that "Information about space, that is, a scientific understanding of cosmic rays, ionization, temperatures, densities in space, is of the utmost importance to us. We must understand the natural laws that will dictate tomorrow's defense."

Another prominent Air Force "space" leader has recently pointed out an avenue to achieve the above-mentioned ends. Major General Bernard A. Schriever, head of the Ballistic Missile Division of the Air Force, stated at the first U. S. Air Force Astronautical Symposium in 1957 that ICBM engines and some of their hardware and components would be available for lunar rockets. He said that "The same propulsive unit that boosts a heavy nose cone warhead 25,000 feet per second, could boost a somewhat lighter body to the escape velocity of 35,000 feet per second or to an orbital path around the earth."

U. S. ICBM's as Large Satellite Launchers

Modifying our ICBM's so that they might boost a larger unmanned satellite into space would be another obvious scientific use for these ultimate weapons. They would be able to carry a solid satellite ball of at least seven times the width of the Vanguard satellite. This larger ball could contain a payload of instruments weighing over a hundred times as much as the first Vanguard orbital package.

With satellites of this size and weight, Earth reconnaissance possibilities for ICBM's loom large in the minds of some scientists, in addition to the already aforementioned "Moon peeking" vehicles.

A large 200- to 300-pound reconnaissance satellite with solar-powered batteries could send back information for a prolonged time as it orbits around the Earth every ninety seconds. The difficulty with this type of utilization lies in the diplomatic and military area, in trying to convince all nations that such reconnaissance satellites would be used *only* for peaceful, scientific views of the Earth to check its oblateness at the poles, to photograph its unexplored territories (of which there are many), etc.

If such an event should come to pass, i.e., using ICBM's to take outer-space pictures of the Earth for scientific purposes only, it will be up to the scientists of the West to help convince their Eastern counterparts of our peaceful intent. This could be accomplished through the channels of international scientific organizations as well as over the diplomatic or military conference tables. A precedent was set in this area when the scientists on both sides of the Iron Curtain agreed in Rome just two short years ago to allow the United States and the Soviet Union to attempt to put up an Earth satellite during the IGY. So a solid foundation has been laid for a much larger step, should it be taken.

Mission to the Moon

The most obvious peaceful, scientific experiment using "modified" ICBM vehicles or components is to launch them from the Earth to circle the Moon. General Bernard A. Schriever, in testimony before the Johnson Senate Preparedness subcommittee in December, 1957, listed several booster applications of present-day IRBM's and ICBM's to expend man into space.

An ICBM orbiting around the Moon could telemeter information back to Earth about what the so-called "dark side" of the Moon is really like. The other side of the Moon, which has never been seen by man, is as big as the North American Continent.

With a zoomar-type television camera in the nose, where normally it would carry a nuclear warhead, an ICBM would become a reconnaissance satellite of the Moon for scientific purposes. The video scanning system would be able to give continuous photographs of areas up to 200,000 square miles, through an orthicon TV unit which would convert telescopic views of the Moon and relay them back to Earth.

A typical ICBM Moon rocket would carry a 200- to 300-pound payload, consisting mainly of cameras and television video tape recorder equipment. General Gregory has predicted that "Certainly we could put a space vehicle on the moon within five years, provided we want to do it."

Moon-circling rockets will differ from those proposed to just "splash" on the Moon, in that they will have to have more energy to return part way to Earth. So they more naturally lend themselves to an ICBM configuration.

Scientific knowledge of the Moon, gained from an ICBM orbiting around it, would benefit the Earth with information in the following areas: the atmosphere of the Moon (if any), its true gravitational pull, its far-side radiation, and the nature of its hydrogen clouds and microwave propagation. General Bernard A. Schriever, before the Johnson committee on December 17, 1957, said, "We could get to the moon by 1959."

The ICBM as a Manned Satellite Booster

It is also theoretically possible, now that Maj. David Simons of the Air Force has successfully ascended in a small gondola to over 100,000 feet in a 32-hour flight, for a man to be tucked into a similar, compact, pressurized and instrumented gondola, which will be carried aloft inside the nose cone of an ICBM instead of by a large plastic balloon.

Granted there are many bugs in such a daring plan, but it should soon be feasible, even to the point of getting him back to Earth. Such a package within a package would be shot straight up for several hundred miles instead of being sent into an orbital trajectory. Such a manned ascent to a 1,000-mile altitude and safe descent back to Earth could be accomplished in less than an hour, compared to Dr. Simon's 32 hours. Obviously the initial test would be made with an ICBM carrying an animal before a man would be sent aloft.

Missions Beyond the Moon

With the successful "boosting" of manned satellites into orbits, simultaneous plans can be made to modify ICBM's to send
man on cross-country and intercontinental flights, and, unmanned, to send small scientific payloads on one-way trips to
Mars and Venus. The knowledge gained from such experiments
would provide valuable data as the necessary forerunner for later
passenger and cargo flights to all points of the world and also
manned flights to the planets.

A Prophecy

If an international agreement can be worked out to utilize
ICBM's and IRBM's for predominantly peaceful, scientific purposes, the revolutionary possibility in the offing for mankind
presents the stark fact that, for the first time in modern history,
a major military weapon will find itself playing a far different
primary role than that for which it was originally intended.

The A-bomb was utilized militarily in the closing days of
World War II on Hiroshima and Nagasaki and has since been
undergoing extensive tests along with its big brother—the H-
bomb—for essentially military purposes. The ICBM's, IRBM's,
however, can be used immediately for scientific purposes after
the bugs have been ironed out in their initial prototype testing.
A scientific utilization of these instruments can be undertaken
along similar lines parallel to the U.S. nuclear programs. We
would not expect a drastic reversal of policy, but rather a slow
transition of application from the military to scientific uses. We
should look at this transition as one means of eliminating expensive storage and overhaul of these rockets. Peaceful ICBM
experiments would be a boon for the scientists, who have enough
present-day difficulties pleading with Congress for a few million
dollars for upper-atmosphere research. They would thus literally
inherit in times of peace (or cold war), billions of dollars worth
of much-needed research and development hardware that has
gone into the big rockets for military ends. The scientists would

be able to use this "ICBM windfall," as the chief means for giving them the know-how that is essential before the true conquest of space becomes a reality.

The cost of scientific adventures into outer space using "modified" ICBM's would be far more than the $110,000,000 expended for the Vanguard Earth satellite program, where approximately half—or $47,000,000—went for the design and construction of a dozen three-stage, satellite-launching vehicles (according to testimony recently given to Congress). It is therefore obvious that only the Federal Government would be capable of organizing and sponsoring such a large-scale, scientific, outer-space program—where the cost would not be reckoned in millions but in billions of dollars. Furthermore, the taxpayer may demand that these ICBM's be put to such worthwhile uses, rather than consigning their short lives to the scrap heap like discarded and outmoded aircraft.

The limitless rewards gained in improved knowledge of meteorology, navigation, medicine, and the Earth itself would be well worth the time and effort put into such a gigantic undertaking. Whether outer-space vehicles are going to be used predominantly for peaceful, scientific ends or only military ones would have a tremendous impact on the direction of the future of civilization. Such a shift from the intended war plans for utilizing Soviet and American long-range rocket vehicles to scientific ends would fulfill a well-known Biblical prophecy of turning "their swords into plowshares, and their spears into pruninghooks." This prophecy is the hope of mankind for survival on Earth.

chapter 5

sputnik's impact on the free world

The shaggiest, lonesomest, saddest dog in all history, reportedly named Limonchik, or Little Lemon, was perhaps, so the dispatch said, a "pet" of one of Russia's ballistic scientists, and was yesterday circling the earth more than 1,000 miles up at the rate of 18,000 miles an hour. Little Lemon, who probably has "a sharp, fox-like face and bright, intelligent eyes," was one of twelve "space dogs" trained to be sent where dogs were never intended to go. Little Lemon was the descendant of some wolf who approached a human campfire many thousands of years ago when somebody tossed him a bone. Yesterday he may have wished his ancestor had stayed in the woods, even though he himself was being fed "a highly calorific liquid" and his heartbeat, breathing, blood pressure and temperature were news around the world wherever the printed word was read or the spoken word widely audible.

The whole future of our own race, Communists and bourgeois alike, the bound and the free, is at stake. Little Lemon, the shaggiest dog, the first real space dog, may be more fortunate than those who sent him aloft, luckier than those in other lands who have to read his portent and take measures accordingly.

But among all the millions and millions of mankind who yesterday stopped their hurrying, or their loitering, or their worrying, or their contemplations and competitions, to learn what was of most interest to them in the whole universe, there was no question where the focus stood. Little Lemon, the unbelievable dog in an incredible predicament, voyaging where, as far as we know, no living creature ever went before, was at the heart and

center of men's thoughts. And Little Lemon, if he had
been asked, would rather have been gnawing a long-
buried bone and trying to catch fleas.

Editorial from
The New York Times—November 5, 1957

T HE streak of white light and the "beep-beep-
beeps" of the first Soviet sputniks in the fall of 1957 served as a
warning to the Free World of the achievement of Russian science
and technology. The West had disregarded all previous signs and
had underestimated the capacity of the Soviet regime to develop instruments like artificial Earth satellites and ICBM's.
But the sputniks' spectacular demonstrations shattered any
doubts that anyone previously had about the state-of-the-
rocket-art behind the Iron Curtain.

Vice President Richard Nixon on October 16, 1957, gave one
of the sanest Administration reactions to sputnik when he said,
"We could make no greater mistake than to brush off this event
as a scientific stunt. . . . We have had a grim and timely reminder . . . that the Soviet Union has developed a scientific
and industrial capacity of great magnitude."

With this sobering statement in mind, it behooves us to take
a long look at some of the changes that the sputniks brought to
various segments and institutions in our culture. The effects of
the sputniks on seven of these most important and interrelated
institutions will be examined in sequence. Strangely enough,
these seven areas form a natural triangle with (1) leadership at
the peak, supported by (2) strategy and tactics, (3) missile production, (4) applied research and development, (5) basic research, (6) educational system, and (7) the democratic culture.

The Sputnik Impact on Western Leadership

Americans seemed to be agreed that what was needed most
after sputnik was proper "leadership" at all levels. Like the na-

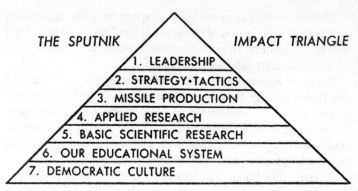

THE SPUTNIK   IMPACT TRIANGLE
1. LEADERSHIP
2. STRATEGY·TACTICS
3. MISSILE PRODUCTION
4. APPLIED RESEARCH
5. BASIC SCIENTIFIC RESEARCH
6. OUR EDUCATIONAL SYSTEM
7. DEMOCRATIC CULTURE

tional recovery after Pearl Harbor, when many leaders came to
the fore, so after sputnik, many prominent Americans, from the
President on down, became outspoken with their recommendations and solutions as to what ought to be done to catch up and
surpass the Soviets in space.

Congressmen, Administration officials, prominent laymen,
news columnists, and many more offered valuable suggestions
on how to climb back out of our dilemma. Complacency van-
ished—slowly after sputnik I, but much more rapidly after the
second satellite launching. The fear of the Soviet ICBM, among
other implications, spurred U.S. leaders to action. The several
Congressional committees that started an investigation of the nation's lag in the missile field performed a service in calming the
people's fears and pointing out ways to get back in the race.

An inspired and dynamic leadership on a sustaining basis at
the top is needed to ensure that the United States achieves that
degree of spacepower, where the citizens once again feel that the
nation's defenses are secure. Such a leadership must take into
cognizance the best scientific advice that can be offered to solve
the myriad problems to be faced in the Space Age. It means
planning, co-ordinating, and capable directing of a program to
conquer space, based on a thoroughly understood set of objectives that the nation itself agrees upon.

This means that an educational program has to be undertaken by the President, leaders of Congress, the military, and the rocket and missile industry to indoctrinate the people in the importance of a well-thought-out space program.

President Eisenhower made a reference in his 1957 State of the Union message that "the cost of peace . . . involves changes in attitudes, the renunciation of old prejudices, even the sacrifice of some seeming self-interest." The impact of the sputniks reaffirmed this portion of his address when the nation reappraised its efforts in science and technology.

Among other things that happened to the United States was the pressure brought by the Administration and certain powerful members of Congress to revise a part of the Atomic Energy Act which forbids the exchange and pooling of scientific knowledge with its Western Allies. It was well known in the fall of 1957 that the United States was leading the West in advancements in rocketry, but that Great Britain was ahead in some branches of radar and air-dropped thermonuclear weapons. So the legal barriers and restrictions that prevented each of these two Western nations from sharing the results of their scientific endeavors were lowering our potential spacepower capacities in the eyes of the rest of the world. One aftereffect of the sputnik shock was the realization that there is merit in the exchange of scientific information with an ally.

Because it was thought that the Soviets were inferior to Americans technologically, there was no reason to pay heed to the seers who were warning about their intellectual advances. The national complacency which was rampant had led everyone to believe that the Russians were "not 10 feet tall," when it actually turned out that some of them were.

Dr. Fritz Zwicky, one of the best basic research minds in the United States, put the blame on the nation's lag in the missile race to an overabundance of "yes" and "no" men. He feels that the reasons why Russia launched the first successful satellite were due to the three following causes:

1. "We have too many 'Yes Men' supporting mediocre or downright worthless scientific projects.

2. "We have too many 'No Men' obstructing or impeding advanced projects.

3. "We have too many people who don't care."

These three assessments of the lack of positive American leadership in the missile field adequately sums up the dilemma.

The leaders in the United States need to be concerned with the welfare of the public institutions, such as the schools, and the military in a more progressive manner than they have in the past. Some of the steps that the nation's leaders were considering or actually made in the reorganization of the rocket and satellite efforts to keep up with the times in the wake of the sputniks were the following:

1. The establishment of a Joint Congressional Committee for Astronautics, similar to the one now in being for atomic energy, to keep a constant finger on the nation's pulse in its progress in space flight. (A Senate Outer-Space Committee was set up in February, 1958.)

2. The establishment of a National Advisory Committee for Astronautics which would be a wholly independent, nonmilitary agency drawing on the best brains from all realms of our culture to make space flight in the United States a top-priority project.

3. The Air Force finally established an Astronautics Division some two months after sputnik I, but it only existed for a "few minutes" as the civilian chiefs in the Department of Defense thought such an act was "premature." This small event was a "birth pang" of the Astronautics Age—not the birth itself.

4. A Department of Science with Cabinet status to assure optimum utilization and efficiency in the technological race. (The appointment of Dr. James R. Killian, Jr., as a Presidential scientific assistant was a step in the right direction.)

5. A series of Congressional investigations into the lag in our missile effort was held by at least four major committees and subcommittees with an emphasis on what could be done to remedy the situation rather than an attempt to fix the blame in some areas for the current lag.

6. The establishment of the Advanced Research Projects Agency in February, 1958, headed by Roy Johnson.

As the needs arise, other major steps will be taken by the Government to meet the challenge of the sputniks. But a warning is in order for the decision makers not to overlook key men with topflight experience in rocketry for administrative posts or consultation in space-flight programs. The tendency to choose non-rocket administrators has hurt many missile programs. Some people have questioned the capabilities of some of our current "space-flight experts" who have been asked by the Government to head a job for which they are not qualified. Rather, the leaders should look among those who have lived with the problem and who have sweated out our past missile programs.

The Sputnik Impact on Western Strategy and Tactics

The Soviets had announced to the world that they successfully fired an ICBM in August, 1957. But the Free World doubted their feat. Sputnik II erased all doubts that anyone might have entertained in the West that Russia had an ICBM. This sobering fact, coupled with our knowledge of the long-range aims of the Soviet Union to conquer the world, has led us to perform many spectacular military propaganda answers to the Soviet challenge. But sending subsonic Snark missiles on a 5,000-mile test flight to Ascension Island or Gen. Curtis LeMay to Argentina in a dramatic round-trip jet flight in the new KC 135 tanker (although a significant display of power) somehow could not match the propaganda significance of the sputniks.

To outmatch the Russians will take more than a panic-type program to show the world our advancements in the science of rocketry. To win the geopolitical and military "battle for outer space," which was the *real* challenge of the sputniks, will take a concerted effort on the part of all elements in the United States. The preparations to wage this "battle" will require that something deliberate and well-planned be done to reaffirm national objectives—*why, when,* and *where* the nation is going in space.

We have already examined the *why* of going into space, but the impact of sputnik has highlighted the *when* and *where*. That is why it is important to examine some of the fundamental institutions in our society which sputnik affected.

The Sputnik Impact on Missile Production

The United States, which prides itself on its ability to outshine the world in mass assembly line production of cars, television sets, freezers, and other gadgets, has been slow to realize that the Soviets have learned to imitate well. Although they have only been able to turn out second-rate consumer goods to date, they have produced first-rate armadas of military aircraft, particularly jets of high quality. They have cut the vital lead time from the birth of an idea to operation drastically below the present rate in the United States.

That they appear to have a lead in production of quantities of long-range rockets was a hard fact to swallow after sputnik. It is well known that they have been able to give centralized direction to both their production techniques and to the technological foundations on which the output is based. The U. S. Government abhorred such centralized production direction at the Federal level for generations. Only in World War II did it show the first signs of industrial mobilization on a grand scale. In more recent times, Washington had looked with disfavor at appointing an industry czar or scientific missile czar, until sputnik forced the issue.

The need to be able to obtain a solution of problems that cut across several military service lines and basic areas of science had been a hope but never a reality before sputnik. To bring together various types of scientists, the separate branches of the armed services, and different industries (including subcontractors), to all work on a common problem had been a hard-to-attain dream in the missile field.

A smooth administrative liaison was lacking between the Government and industries engaged in high-priority, "crash" defense projects, particularly in the rocket field. The lack of a missile czar to ride herd over the production of ICBM's and IRBM's as well as the newer missiles and space vehicles was glaringly apparent

within a short time after sputnik's lessons had been driven home
to an awakened United States.

The Sputnik Impact on Science: Applied Research and Development

In the search for a national scapegoat after sputnik, an accusing finger invariably turned toward American science. What was
the thinking behind these accusations?

The public tendency to regard our scientists as "eggheads" or
"longhairs" was cited shortly after sputnik's advent, by Dr. B. D.
Thomas, director of the Battelle Memorial Institute, as a prime
reason for a shortage of engineers and scientists in the United
States. He said that the lack of prestige and public sympathy for
scientists and their achievements were more responsible for the
failure to attract young people into these important fields than
greater financial rewards. Granting more awards and honors to
rocket scientists should help regain lagging prestige. This step
should help to make science careers more rewarding.

Dean John R. Dunning of Columbia University, a leading
atomic physicist, has a similar view, that not only should the public change its smug attitude toward scientists, but that the Government, education, and industry should change their attitude
also. Until all agencies in society adopt a more favorable attitude
toward scientists, the United States can never hope to catch up
with the Soviets.

There will have to be an increase in the scientists' salaries, not
only so they can continue in research efforts without fear of
financial insecurity, but also to make it possible for them to teach
in the schools and colleges on a part-time, or a full-time basis.
When we raise the prestige and salaries of mathematics and science teachers in the public schools, it will be possible to reattract
some of the better science teachers who have gone into industry.

The country may not be able to catch up in the quantity of
scientists produced, but it can plan to surpass the Soviets in the
quality of engineers who are graduated yearly. This is the hope
for the United States in the greatest challenge that it has faced

as a young nation, the challenge of technological supremacy.

The appointment of Dr. James R. Killian, Jr., president of Massachusetts Institute of Technology, as President Eisenhower's scientific adviser soon after sputnik, and the naming of a new Department of Defense civilian space manager, Roy Johnson, indicated the increased importance of scientists in the Government.

These moves also signified that something was finally being done to lessen the degree of interservice rivalry that had been apparent in certain areas of national defense. The signs of surface shakeups in the Pentagon and elsewhere in the Government were an obvious attempt to accomplish what money alone couldn't buy. The end to be achieved was and is the regaining of the lead in world science, which was once held by the United States.

The sputniks also brought about a belated end to the artificial barrier that had been erected between the scientists and the military before and during the early days of the International Geophysical Year of 1957–58. The granting of a go-ahead to the Army to provide a supplementary satellite launcher with its military Jupiter C rocket by the Secretary of Defense within a month after the first sputnik was launched symbolized the end to what *The New York Times* called . . . "the naive assumption that the [Vanguard] program is a purely scientific enterprise that should not be contaminated with such mundane things as political and military considerations."

The announcement on November 18, 1957, that the International Geophysical Year Committee of the National Academy of Sciences had transferred one of the original Earth satellite experiments on cosmic rays from the Navy to the Army, with its Jupiter C satellite rocket launcher, was a vivid example of this shift in policy. Subsequently, the Explorer I, launched by the Jupiter C, showed us that reasonable human survival temperatures between 45 degrees and 90 degrees Fahrenheit can be maintained inside a satellite or future manned spaceships. A mixed organization composed of military and civilian scientists appears to be needed to implement the integration of the scientist and the military officer. A combination of the sense of mission plus a scientific insight with the *proper* and unique administrative environment is essential to make this integration function properly.

Another allied scientific area, where sputnik appeared to have a significant impact, was in modifying the nation's own internal Iron Curtain, in presenting the increased dissemination of the fruits of applied research. *The New York Herald Tribune* challenged the Government to "break down the senseless walls of super secrecy which are keeping nothing from the Soviets but preventing our own scientists from cross-fertilizing each other's ideas. . . ."

By putting loyalty ahead of brains and constructive thinking, the U. S. Government found itself stymied when it needed proper advice and help. The suspicion of scientists who posed an original thought and the general lack of respect for them in the community forced many good men out of the Government. In the Soviet Union, on the other hand, it is an honor to be a professor, and the leading scientists are universally recognized and well paid.

The noted seer, Walter Lippmann, in a thought-provoking column written soon after sputnik, philosophized that "What McCarthyism did to the inner confidence of the American scientists and thinkers has constituted one of the great national tragedies of the postwar era. It is impossible to measure the damage. But the damage that was done was very great. It was done in the kind of thinking where the difference between creation and routine lies in the special courage to follow the truth wherever it leads." And Representative John Moss of California, chairman of the House Information subcommittee, said at a recent hearing that "a blanket of (Government) secrecy is stifling scientific advance" in the United States.

It appeared that the results of free science in the West, with its imposed mantle of Government secrecy restrictions, had finished a poor second to the totalitarian science of the Communist World, which somehow had been able to break through the West's internal secrecy barriers. The knowledge that Russia employs hundreds of translators to interpret Western technical

Fig. 5—A satellite's impact on our economic life, predicting a hurri-
cane and advance weather warning.

Fig. 6—Social and legal problems would result from many satellites orbiting at the same time in space.

abstracts for their scientists' benefit should be a challenge to the United States to provide a similar communications and abstract translation service for its scientists.

What is needed is establishment of the proper atmosphere so the scientists feel that they will not be treated with suspicion when they propose some step forward that is "new." Such an inspirational atmosphere is necessary to instill enthusiasm and boost the morale of the many scientists working on hundreds of important defense projects.

The former aura of doubt and irrelevancy on the part of high-level officials concerning the ideas of those who propounded space-flight programs was dramatically erased by the sputniks. The regulation which prohibited Air Force officers and officials from mentioning or discussing "space flight," was an example of a suppression of free individual expression that was carried to an extreme.

With the current battle for the minds of men in the background of the surface race for technological superiority, it becomes a must to provide a relatively free atmosphere for our scientists and space-flight enthusiasts to function properly. As Senator Lyndon Johnson said during the post-sputnik committee hearings: "There is no security in any one weapon. The real security lies in a highly trained corps of engineers and scientists capable of meeting any threats."

The Sputnik Impact on Science: Basic Research

One of the first acts of the U. S. Government after it recovered from the shock of the first sputnik was to restore $170,000,000 of vitally needed funds to the USAF Office of Scientific Research for basic research contracts to various universities and responsible agencies. Unfortunately, most of the public, some Administration officials, and many members of Congress had not properly understood the role of basic research in our society. The rising costs of the research and development programs had been looked upon with a hatchet eye by many members of the economy-minded Congress and was a fertile field for cutbacks.

Applied research was the more common type of research, where the Government underwrote a specific project for a specific purpose with a specific amount of money and a specific deadline to be met. Most of these contracts were in the military realm of advanced weaponry or its supporting enterprises, which would benefit one or all of the three armed services.

But scientists had known for a long time that you cannot put an engineer into a hopper, turn a few dials, and guarantee an answer in a prescribed amount of time. Automation has never been able to take over completely the workings of the human mind. No computer yet invented can perform some of the intricate functions that are necessary to solve the problems of applied research. However, the critical area was not in the applied zone of research, where adequate funds appeared to be the order of the day, but rather in the nebulous zone of basic scientific research. Professor Nickolai Muckelishvili, president of the Soviet Georgian Academy of Science, stated recently that the American setbacks are due to "a certain disregard for theoretical research and to attaching too much importance to empirical, purely practical methods."

Basic (or fundamental) research differs from the predominant *applied* form, in that there is usually no time limit to solving any prescribed problem. In fact, the *problems* aren't even prescribed in most cases. Rather, scientists delving into basic research set up their own objectives or just experiment in their subject fields to discover more unknowns. Whether they come up with anything of value to mankind is not important in basic research.

A Defense Department directive of November 13, 1957, in which basic research was defined for the *first* time in a Government policy directive, ignored any mention of a military application. The official definition stated that "*Basic research is that type of research which is directed toward increase of knowledge of science. It is research where the primary aim of the investigator is a fuller knowledge or understanding of the subject under study.*" (Authors' italics.)

However, the Pentagon acknowledged that this type of research is important to the defense effort in an indirect way, as it is an "essential ingredient in potential military power as opposed to military power in being." Extending this phrase to include spacepower makes basic research all the more important when we consider the future of space flight.

A good example of how basic research pays dividends to the defense effort is in the area of exotic fuels for rockets. (Exotic fuels are defined as fuels that yield *significantly* higher performance over the best fuels obtainable today.) For the past decade, researchers in the Johns Hopkins University, under Dr. Walter S. Koski, have been experimenting with mixing and tearing apart boron hydride compounds.

These compounds were highlighted in the news following the launching of sputnik II with speculation that they might have been the superfuel used to launch the rocket that carried Laika into her orbit around the Earth.

Long before the engineering and propulsion needs of space vehicles could have been anticipated, basic research scientists learned that boron hydrides give out immense heat when burned. Because of the light mass of the boron combustion particles, they provided more thrust when burned in a rocket engine.

Actually the basic research in this new exotic fuel has been going on for half a century. The scientists at Johns Hopkins, though, working with the aid of a chemical firm's grant and support from the Air Force, are *not* seeking to invent a new rocket fuel, but rather are continuing their basic studies into the nature of compounds. . . . What makes the molecules hold together? Why do they split in certain ways? This is the stuff of basic research which *may* or *may not* have a military application later on.

The basic research division of a forward-looking industry like General Electric's Research Laboratories is but one example of enlightened present-day thinking and application in this vital area.

More funds for basic research as well as a full interchange among scientists of the results of the research are two important steps that need to be taken to regain the lost leadership in the realm of outer space. Better communication, including more funds for translations and interpreters of foreign scientific documents should be in order to implement the foundations of a well-planned national basic research program.

But the taxpayers and economy-minded Congressmen and Administration officials had generally looked with a critical eye on Government-sponsored financial efforts to aid basic research for the following reason: "Why waste money on a project that might not pay off?" The Manhattan Project that gave the atomic bomb and nuclear fission was applied research under pressure. Yet it was the fruits of years of painstaking basic research on the part of many world physicists that made this project and its successful culmination possible.

In the field of rocketry and missiles, all the billions that were spent on a crash (applied research) program to launch successfully a test IRBM and an ICBM ahead of the Soviets did not produce results in time to win the initial lap of the long-range missile race. In the race for space, the United States fell behind in the eyes of the rest of the world, when the two sputniks were launched in the fall of 1957. In the assessment that followed as to why we lost, it appeared that both *applied* and *basic* research were partly at fault, even though hundreds of engineers and scientists were working overtime to produce successful test missiles ahead of the Russians.

This "sputnik Pearl Harbor," as one prominent slick magazine put it in its lead editorial, was a more direct result, among other factors, of not having an adequate basic research program to supplement and back up the expansive undertakings in the applied military field. Had the United States pursued such a balanced course in research endeavors after World War II, instead of putting most of its eggs in the surface applied research basket, the nation might have beaten the Soviets into space.

What is needed, then, is a well-planned national program for encouraging, financing, and fostering basic research in all the sciences.

The Sputnik Impact on Education

Success or failure to produce worthwhile dividends from large undertakings in both basic and applied research, particularly as they apply to outer-space programs, will depend entirely on the health of the educational system in the United States.

For decades, school experts and educators have been warning about the growing plight and crisis of the educational system, from which are provided the scientists of tomorrow. Unfortunately, neither the Congress nor the nation has come to the aid of the beleaguered schools to solve this increasing problem. Because of seemingly unsolvable conflicts between religious pressure groups, business and labor groups, and segregation and integration groups, every Federal school aid bill of note that has been introduced in one or more of the Houses of Congress over the past half century has been killed.

The complacency on the part of the people and their leaders over taking a giant step toward improving the school system has been apparent on all levels of the Government. It took the sputniks, though, finally to awaken the lawmakers and leaders to the fact that these other issues which divided Americans in the past were now secondary to that of the paramount issue . . . national survival. For this reason, it appears that for the first time in the 20th century, the United States is not only going to take a long hard look at its school system and *talk* about it, but actually will *do* something constructive in a big way to rectify its failings.

Such a massive multibillion-dollar Federal aid legislation to bring the public educational system out of the second-rate doldrums where it has been languishing for years, would envision not only aid for school construction alone, but also funds to aid *all* teachers (not just science and mathematics instructors). The morale of the rest of the school faculty would be seriously impaired if the prestige of the science instructors was exalted above the others. Sputnik, therefore, has brought about a much greater understanding of the need for qualified teachers in *all* fields of education.

The immediate impact of sputnik on education was to focus

the attention of the nation on the shortage of science and mathematics teachers. At the same time, attention was given to that well-trained and poorly paid group who are trying to inspire would-be Einsteins, Tellers, and Oppenheimers of tomorrow in inadequate classrooms with improper equipment.

On November 30, 1957, President Eisenhower's special study committee on scientists and engineers reported that in response to the Soviet threat in this Space Age, that the United States must marshal "our brainpower resources in company with other nations of the free world—not only for mutual defense but to meet the broader challenges of the scientific age."

This tall order hints at a sort of "sputnik-centered curriculum" in our schools in order to meet this challenge. Such a curriculum would envision improvement of both elementary and secondary education with inevitable emphasis on the sciences. Encouragement to adopt this curriculum would be given not only at the Federal level through the help of the National Science Foundation, but also at the State and local level through the broader participation of industrial, labor, professional, and educational groups to help plan the Space Age curriculum for tomorrow. (*See* Chap. 15.)

Allen Dulles, the head of the U. S. Central Intelligence Agency, stated before the Senate Preparedness subcommittee that "to improve scientific education in the U.S., we would have to stress the importance of science to security." He told the committee that in contrast to the United States, "*every* Russian student, by the time he finishes high school, has had five years of physics, five of biology, four of chemistry, and ten of mathematics." Why could this nation not plan a similar curriculum for *all* of our qualified scientific-minded students? A curriculum which would go beyond the present-day scientific disciplines mentioned above, to include the newer astronautical disciplines still in their infancy.

The Challenge of the Sputniks to the Democratic Culture

Mr. Donald K. David, the chairman of the board of trustees for the Committee for Economic Development and the former Dean of the Harvard University Graduate School of Business Administration, made an astute observation on sputnik in connection with an announcement of a $500,000 grant from the Ford Foundation to study the private and public monetary policies of the United States. His observation made on November 18, 1957, deserves to be read and digested by every American—and particularly those who have only learned a part of the lesson of the sputnik. He said:

> Like all of you, I am not deaf to the whirr of man-made satellites above us. It has already become a cliché that Sputnik will be a blessing if it awakens America. This is true—if it awakens us to the right lesson. The real lesson of Sputnik is the lesson of applying systematic thought and knowledge to the solution of major national problems. . . . Behind Sputnik, we see a rocket, and behind the rocket we see advanced science and technology. However, there is something more behind this. There is a social system of human institutions that, in this case, has made the correct decision about what was important to achieve and has motivated and organized efforts to achieve it.

This is the challenge of sputnik. The issue is not just one of stepping up the missiles program to see who "gets there fustest with the mostest" in a sort of panic race to oblivion, but rather, it is a wider and deeper issue that involves all Americans and their educational system, their attitudes, their willingness to examine themselves and their culture, and their obligation to meet the challenge of their fast-changing society.

For instance, the American Institute of Public Opinion (Gallup Poll) in mid-December, 1957, discovered that more than five million Americans are willing to take a fling at space travel —even if it's a one-way trip. Twice as many young people as older folks were intrigued by the prospective adventures in space, and appeared to give little heed to the problems of getting home unscathed. How many would have volunteered for space flight before sputnik?

Finally, one of the major problems of the Space Age of tomorrow as far as the Western World is concerned is the post-sputnik dilemma of whether or not the Western democracies can keep ahead of Communist Russia in scientific fields (including rocketry) without sacrificing their prized freedoms in the process. To cope with a society whose leaders can mobilize all of that society's resources to attain her set scientific and military goals is a supreme challenge for the United States and its Allies.

A clue to the solution of this dilemma was given a decade ago by Edward Hallett Carr, the noted British political scientist, in his little book, *The Soviet Impact on the Western World*, where he propounded the theory that whereas our impact on the Soviet Union was our *freedoms*, the Soviet impact on the West was *planning*. It is therefore up to us to become accustomed to the fact that we must *plan* to achieve those essential goals in rocketry, where our survival is at stake, without losing our cherished freedoms in the bargain.

If we can find a middle ground of planning for the general welfare by mobilizing our society, including our educational system, at only the expense of losing some of our more obvious (and unnecessary) individual items of conspicuous consumption, then we can be assured that our best abilities are devoted to the tasks on which our freedom depends. Such losses of the material frills of our society are not as important as losses of our most precious freedoms, which would be a tragic loss.

It is up to us to meet the Soviet challenge not only to guarantee our survival and status as a first-rate power, but to help lead the world into a peaceful era of space flight without the threat of war to mar such exploration. "Business as usual" will not be adequate to meet this challenge.

Secretary of State, John Foster Dulles, in a speech before the National Press Club in Washington on January 16, 1958, cogently summed up sputnik's impact on the Western World, when he said: "The launching of an earth satellite by the Soviets may mark a decisive turn in the world-wide struggle between Communist imperialism and the free world.

"No doubt the Communist rulers gained a success. They have an opportunity to gloat, an opportunity that they have not neglected. But sputnik, mocking the American people with its 'beep-beep,' may go down in history as Mr. Khrushchev's boomerang.

"It jolted the American people and produced a reaction which was healthy, the kind of reaction that has, in the past, served freedom well. A wave of mortification, anger and fresh determination swept the country. Out of that mood is coming a more serious appraisal of the struggle in which we are engaged, and an increasing willingness to make the kind of efforts and sacrifices needed to win that struggle."

Framing the Triangle

Now that we have surveyed the impact of sputnik on seven basic institutions within our cultural triangle, let us look at the more nebulous frame of the triangle—the social impact of Earth satellites on society. To understand this more intangible area is a must if we wish truly to appreciate the overwhelming effect of the sputniks now and in the future on all phases of our civilization.

chapter 6

satellites and society

Heard the heavens fill with shouting, and
    there rain'd a ghastly dew
From the nations' airy navies grappling in
    the central blue;
Far along the world-wide whisper of the
    south-wind rushing warm,
With the standards of the peoples plung-
    ing thro' the thunder-storm;
Till the war-drum throbb'd no longer, and
    the battle-flags were furl'd
In the Parliament of man, the Federation
    of the world.
                Alfred Lord Tennyson
                "Locksley Hall"

IN THE preceding chapter, we explored the direct impact of the sputniks on the Free World, now let us look at the still-unannounced (and relatively unexplored) social impacts of the satellites on man. The social results will occur simultaneously with the scientific experiments, but will undoubtedly not be assessed till many years later. In this respect, the social-cultural lag following the technological changes which the satellites symbolize, will probably follow the patterns of other significant scientific breakthroughs of the past.

The social impact of man's first step into space covers such divergent areas as improved mass communication, changes in economy, the exploration of space, and the satellites' influence on world peace. Now let us examine these four areas in detail.

Improved Mass Communication

To achieve exactly a 24-hour circular orbit, the "stationary" satellite must be at a radical distance of 26,250.5 miles from the center of the Earth or 22,291.6 miles distant from the Earth's surface—traveling at a velocity of 10,079.5 feet per second. The satellite would then have a period of 86,400 seconds or 24 hours.

If we place three, 24-hour "stationary" satellites of the Earth into orbit over the equator at approximately 120 degrees apart, then the first truly transglobal communication link will be established. A communication link of this type could be used for hundreds of simultaneous telephone conversations between continents. In order to understand the principle behind the operation of this type of communication link, let us look briefly at the billiard ball analogy. If we pretend that the satellite is a billiard ball and then aim a radio signal at it which will in turn carom off the satellite's smooth skin to a receiving station on the other side of the globe, we have an explanation of how this phenomenon would occur in reality. There is presently available microwave radio equipment, such as directional disc-shaped antennas, which would focus the ultra short wave (microwaves) in a concentrated beam directly on the satellite. Although these highly reliable radio impulses would be reflected in all directions, a large portion could be picked up by sensitive high gain antennas.

Thus, another barrier to faster social communications between the nations of the Earth will be overcome. This particular application of satellites to improve mass telephonic, radio, and television communication between the continents involves several obvious problems. First, we would need quite a large satellite. The experimental rubber and plastic inflatable satellites which are now undergoing tests by the National Advisory Committee for Aeronautics offer a possible solution to this problem. These large balls, covered with aluminum foil, are called corner reflectors because of their peculiar shape, which is most capable of reflecting radio signals.

We may find, though, as we become more familiar with the behavior of satellites, that it would be simpler and more economical to use many smaller spheres at lower altitudes. We would lose the advantage of using a relatively motionless body at 22,000 miles, but the movement of the smaller spheres would be fairly regular, and the transmitting antennas might be adjusted to track one satellite after another as they drifted overhead in their orbits.

Whichever method is used, it is safe to say that satellites will usher in the first true worldwide communications network.

A universal series of radio and television networks circling the globe will be possible as a result of simultaneous global ocean-spanning television with satellites acting as relay stations. For the first time, man will immediately be able to *see* as well as *hear* events taking place anywhere on the Earth's surface. This fact should help diplomats prevent trouble spots from erupting into "brush fire" wars or global conflicts.

Arthur C. Clarke of the British Interplanetary Society, in his new book, *The Making of a Moon*, philosophizes about the political and moral consequences of the satellite's erasing the communications distance barrier between nations. He writes:

> The political (consequences) are obvious; the moral ones perhaps less so. But if anyone doubts they exist, let him consider what might happen to the audience rating of the average American or British TV show if it had to compete with the program which certain less inhibited countries might transmit.
>
> Although the first satellites will be primarily the concern of science, the later ones may affect directly the lives of every man on Earth—if not in the manner suggested above (international TV), then in ways which we cannot fully anticipate today. The social consequences of any invention or discovery can never be foreseen; their ripples spread far beyond the original point of application. The men who perfected the typewriter never dreamed that a major result of their work would be the independence and the ultimate equality of women, nor could Henry Ford have guessed how the mobility he gave the world was to change the pattern of society.

As the world will be shrunk to the size of a small city, communications-wise, when satellites become a common occurrence, it behooves us to ponder the import of Clarke's words.

Changes in Our Economic Orbit

The social impact of satellites on society cannot be divorced from economics. For instance, improved long-range weather forecasting will be made possible by satellite scientific data relayed back to Earth, and will help to revolutionize the food and fiber industries, among others. Crop planting times can be gauged better than the present hit-or-miss methods of farming. Better prediction and control of the weather will be the biggest boon to farmers since the invention of the plow.

Arthur C. Clarke in his aforementioned book prophesied that: "It is perhaps in the field of meteorology that the [meteorological] space station will have the most direct impact on human life. . . . The time may be not very far in the future when everyone can rely completely on the forecast for several days ahead, and even long range prediction of major changes may become possible. The economic importance of such service is *so enormous that it would not take a meteorological space station very long to pay for itself.*" (Authors' italics.)

Long-range accurate weather forecasting will have its effect on summer and winter vacations. Increased traffic jams on hot summer days can be eliminated in years to come with families leaving for the shore or mountains *before* a weekend rush as a result of better long-range weather prognosticating. With more leisure time as a result of automation, people can take advantage of good weather during the middle of the week as well as weekends. Some business concerns might find it wise to plan for snowy and icy periods by staggering their working hours—thus spreading out peak traffic flows and helping to reduce the inevitable bad weather traffic jams. Satellites could also light a city all night by creating an artificial air glow—an example of harnessing the weather.

Another change in the economy will come about as a result of the financial outlay for satellites. A comprehensive and realistic space satellite and space-travel program, because of the complexity and enormous costs involved, can best be undertaken on a multinational level under United Nations sponsorship. The

United States portion of such a top-priority crash space program would tax its economy as no event since World War II, but there does not appear to be any reason to fear a depression as a result of controlled budgetary expenditures.

If the United States decided to "go it alone," the economic challenges of the exploration of space could so affect the national budgetary expenditures that there might not be enough tax money left to expend on great amounts of military weapons without a tightening of the national money belt somewhere along the line. If this situation comes about, the essentials of individual welfare should not be sacrificed.

Although the United States has proved to the world that it can sustain a cold-war economy, by producing an adequate supply of military weapons and civilian goods at the same time, there is a serious question as to whether it could maintain a triple program of consumer goods, guns, *and* spaceships without a possible shortage occurring in some of the former items.

It has been estimated by Alton Blakeslee, the Associated Press science writer, that the cost of the satellite program amounts to less than 5 cents for each United States taxpayer. The typical "man on the street" will take this assessment without many questions or criticisms. He will probably not ask, "What's in it for me?" as long as such a program remains under a $100,000,000 total. But an extension of the satellite program to a Moon rocket, for example, would cost the American taxpayer an estimated $2,000,000,000, according to Dr. Walter Dornberger, former head of the V-2 project, and Comdr. Robert Truax, former president of the American Rocket Society. However, with the present state-of-the-art, this figure might be cut to $200,000,000.

The American people would undoubtedly ask questions about such expenditures. Their approval of such astronomical sums will depend largely on the success of the present satellite program.

With scientific know-how on the brink of many important breakthroughs which might lead to manned space flight within years instead of decades, then a good case can be made for an all-out effort now.

Social Problems in the Exploration of Space

People who are disturbed by the implications of space exploration would be comforted by Dr. Franklyn M. Branley, associate astronomer of the American Museum of Natural History and the Hayden Planetarium in New York City who recently stated that:

> There is another reason for exploring space which has nothing to do with science. Its province is poetry, philosophy, or better still, the heart of man. It is simply that our deep hunger for knowledge and conquest must be appeased. This hunger has taken men to the top of Everest, to the deeps of the seas and the poles. Now it will lead us into space. The enormous interest of Americans in space travel is proof that we all feel this urge to explore new worlds. It is the next step in our endless march.

Once space exploration begins in earnest, it is reasonable to suppose that we will find some worlds naturally suitable for habitation. We may very well find some of these worlds already inhabited with rational creatures who may not be radically different in physique from the human race. Indeed the more we learn about ourselves and nature, the less likely it appears that we are alone in the Universe. If many of man's activities are discovered being carried on by other beings in other worlds of the galaxy, then we will have to adjust to their galactic folkways and mores as they will to ours.

Dr. Donald N. Michael, Senior Research Associate, Dunlap and Associates, Inc., Stamford, Connecticut, has proposed a program for research into the impact of satellites on society. He states: "We have the opportunity to follow the evolution of behavior, values and beliefs as they change into new species or become extinct, under the influences of technical modifications for example, the unmanned satellite becoming the manned one. We can study this evolution as it occurs. And possibly, more important of all, we can for the first time in history do detailed studies on the states of mind, values and fantasies of people *before* they are exposed to a new development as well as after. Thus we can get the first half of a before-after research design so crucial to hypothesis testing in all fields, and so especially difficult to realize in the area of social change."

Such a continuing series of studies would make important contributions not only to our understanding of the dynamics of social change, but also to our application of social science in devising new theories for understanding the ways in which societies change.

Satellites as Peaks of Peace

Man is a curious, aggressive animal, who is never satisfied until he has conquered something that he has set his mind to. An example of such a terrestrial success, after many previously attempted failures and tragedies, was his final conquest of the highest point on Earth in 1953—Mount Everest. When Sir Edmund Hillary and Tensing Norkay finally reached the 29,000-foot summit, they planted four flags on an icy, snowy peak on the highest elevation of the Himalayas. These flags, wrapped around the handle of an ice ax, were those of Great Britain, India, Nepal, and the United Nations. This last flag was significant, for it marked the first time that a previously unexplored portion of the Earth had been conquered in the name of some higher agency than that of a single sovereign nation.

Thus, the conquest of Everest represented, in a sense, a Peak of Peace to mankind. The significance of the victorious assault was not a military one, but demonstrated that man could do something constructive and peaceful without thoughts of partisan aggrandizement as his primary aim. Similarly, the conquest of space, beginning first with unmanned satellites, can serve peaceful ends instead of being an instrument of a military victory.

There is hope that with successful satellites circling in their orbits most men will be so intent on the peaceful conquest and exploration of the mysteries of outer space, that they will lift their eyes vertically toward new goals, and away from horizontal concentration on providing bigger and deadlier deterrents to ward off earthbound opponents.

In his quest for more and more scientific knowledge about

cosmic rays, the Earth's magnetic field, measurement of interplanetary dust, man might become so intensively embroiled in probing the answers to the questions about these scientific phenomena, that he will gradually reduce his concentration on weapons of war. President Eisenhower, in hailing the start of the International Geophysical Year of 1957–58, made the following statement on the eve of the official opening on July 1, 1957. After pointing out that the IGY was a great example "of the ability of peoples of all nations to work together harmoniously for the common good," he continued that, "I hope this can become common practice in other fields of human endeavor. . . . The scientists tell us that they cannot possibly anticipate all of the valuable scientific knowledge that will result from their efforts. They believe that many of the facts thus acquired will give us new understanding and new power over the forces of nature."

However, the most important result of the IGY may be the demonstration of the ability of peoples of all nations to work together harmoniously for the common good. The interdependence of the peoples of the Earth will become increasingly apparent as the satellites continue to spin in their orbits.

Professor Leonid Sedov, a leading Soviet space authority, echoed this feeling when he stated recently that Soviet scientists hope development of the satellite "will serve as a basis for peaceful competition for the beginning of joint efforts in the solution of the great tasks of interplanetary travel of the future. . . ."

A Long-Range Satellite Program

Admiral Alfred Mahan in his classic book, *The Influence of Seapower upon History, 1660–1783,* devoted a chapter to the internal, psychological effects of England's decision to command the seas. A similar sociopsychological issue faces the superpowers in the forthcoming conquest of space.

Mahan's warning against complacency and smugness in regard to naval superiority applies equally well to the problem of satellites, space stations and ICBM's. In other words, it will not benefit Russia just to be able to say, "We launched the first successful Earth-circling satellite." The initial prestige which came to the Soviet Union could soon be lost without a dynamic follow-up policy to pursue the logical next steps in the conquest of man's last frontier.

A post-IGY plan to carry on the pioneering which has begun with the present satellite program is essential. Such a program would be operated and financed much like the U. S. Social Security program. In a sense, an investment in a permanent Earth satellite program will extend the security of the United States and the rest of the world.

In a significant article entitled "Reflections on Sea and Space" in the *Saturday Review*, Peter Ritner aptly summed up the present space exploration dilemma when he wrote:

> Admiral Mahan was neither the first nor the last philosopher to realize that new rules make a new game. We Americans are playing today with new cards and for new stakes. Only a generation of gamblers and pioneers—such as we must again become —can hope to enjoy the game.

Since history has no precedent for the situation of a nation setting out to destroy another when its own destruction would certainly follow, then there are real grounds for faith that we may be facing a prolonged era of world peace at last. The social results of the scientific advances of the IGY will not be assessed or held to an eighteen-month timetable, but will have their continuing and growing impact on man as long as he inhabits the Earth. Satellites and space vehicles may become the chief lever for bringing about the brotherhood of man on Earth.

chapter 7

wanted: an international lunar project

I am sure that it [a moon trip] will have a great practical advantage. I am sure it will have a great peaceful advantage, and that it will have a great military advantage. . . . I can't tell you on black and white what will be the advantages of moon trips—some may be amusing—*but there are advantages!* (Authors' italics.)

Dr. Edward Teller
Father of the H-bomb
Before the Johnson committee—November 25, 1957

The Current Interest in the Moon

ALL eyes are on the Moon nowadays. Now that man has successfully placed several satellites in orbit, the question most often asked is: "Will the Moon be the next goal in space?" Travel to the Moon can be and probably will be the beginning of the greatest adventure that man will undertake in this century.

As Gen. Omar Bradley, the retired Chairman of the Joint Chiefs of Staff, said recently: "Up to ten years ago, all this talk about going to the moon . . . was just dreams. I don't think it is a dream anymore." As General Bradley implied, going to the Moon is now a reality.

Before sputnik I, both American and Russian authorities were predicting that the first unmanned rocket to the Moon would

probably not be launched until sometime *after* 1970. But events
since October 4, 1957, changed that thinking radically and time-
tables for unmanned and manned lunar vehicles have been
stepped up tremendously.

It is perfectly logical that this concentration of the world's
scientists, military leaders, and politicians should be centered
on the Moon. The Moon, our own natural satellite, is a blood
relative of the Earth, probably having been born at the same
time. It is 2,160 miles wide, just a little more than one-fourth
of the Earth's diameter. The Moon's orbit is an ellipse of small
eccentricity, 0.05490 in the average. As a result of this eccentricity, the Moon's distance from the Earth ranges from 221,000-
plus miles to 252,000-plus miles. The orbital velocity is slightly
greater than 3,300 feet per second; the escape velocity approximately 7,870 feet per second; and the orbital sideral period (one
complete revolution around the Earth), somewhat greater than
27 days, 7 hours, 43 minutes.

When the Sun shines on the Moon's surface it becomes extremely hot, having a temperature well above the boiling point
of water. When the Sun sets, the Moon's surface becomes extremely cold, dropping close to absolute zero. The first Moon
explorers or "lunarians" will initially have to prepare to exist
under these temperature extremes. Temperature will be one of
the major factors affecting the design of lunarian shelters.

Some of the advantages of establishing a permanent lunar
base as opposed to the space station concept are as follows:

1. From a military standpoint, lunar bases are not as vul-
   nerable to counteractions as are space stations.
2. Medical aspects of a lunar base are much better; i.e., protection from the effects of cosmic rays, etc.
3. The Moon has the advantage of moderate gravitation.
4. The Moon's size makes it much easier to accommodate
   growth and expansion of required facilities.
5. The Moon's surface may contain materials that would help
   alleviate the supply problem.
6. The Moon offers more possible solutions to such basic problems as waste disposal.

7. Psychologically, the Moon may be a better space station, in that it offers firm ground under the spaceman's feet.

8. The Moon offers a natural staging area and an opportunity to build spaceports for exploration of the Universe.

9. The Moon is also recognized by many as a potential world scientific research center.

So with all eyes on the Moon, the next question which concerns us is: "How will we get there?" Let us look at several, generally accepted steps which comprise *one way* of getting to the Moon.

Through the years, rocket experts from many nations have proposed numerous scientific Moon missions for both unmanned and manned lunar vehicles. Presented below, in four sequential phases, are these classical missions.

The First Missions to the Moon

Phase I. Different types of unmanned lunar probes. These probes are designed to fulfill several basic but important missions. The first probe would impact on the Moon with an explosive payload, which could be seen from the Earth as a flash of light against the dark lunar surface. An alternative type of explosive charge could be carbon black or any other dense pigment that could be utilized as a dye marker. An explosive charge would spread such a dye marker over a large area of the Moon's surface. The prime objective of such an impact probe would be to demonstrate that the Moon can be reached by man or his instruments. As simple as this step sounds, it should be remembered that the Moon is an extremely small and fast-moving body. Therefore, to hit the Moon the trajectory calculations must be precise.

The second type of lunar probe would be geared for *lunar reconnaissance*. Since the Moon has a moderate gravitational field compared to the Earth, the reconnaissance probe must have a precise lunar approach velocity. If the approach velocity exceeds a certain upper limit, then the reconnaissance probe will not be captured by the Moon's gravitational field but will shoot past it. It would carry a moderate payload and have as its objective the collection of information about the Moon's surface, atmosphere, size, etc.

In its flight path around the Moon, the vehicle could conceivably photograph the far side of its surface, which has never been seen. It is presumed that this pass will be made when the dark side of the Moon is in sunlight so that the cameras can record what is there. The data could be collected in one of two ways: by telemetering from the vehicle in flight, or by building the lunar probe to survive re-entry and a landing on the Earth. The manner of data collection would depend for one thing on the solution of the re-entry problem.

Controlling a probe's return to Earth will present many problems and will be extremely critical. As the probe falls in its earthbound trajectory for 257,000 miles, it could conceivably gain sufficient speed, so that if left unchecked, it could theoretically overshoot the Earth and go out in the other direction to the Moon's orbit.

The third type of probe could be a *lunar satellite*. Assuming that the Moon can be reached with a large enough payload, it should be possible to establish a radar beacon or a telemetering station in a satellite orbit around the Moon. This orbit should be stable, since the Moon's atmosphere is certainly very thin if it exists at all. The scientific information that could be collected in this way would be invaluable.

Some typical experiments that can be considered for the lunar probes are as follows:

To photograph the solar corona and prominences, and on the same trip photograph the dark side of the Moon. The solar corona is of extreme importance to astrophysicists.

To measure lunar surface radiations, both atomic and electromagnetic, and also to measure temperatures. (The Moon's surface may be radioactive.)

To measure lunar magnetism.

To determine ionization in lunar "atmosphere." (Though the Moon has little or no atmosphere, it is believed that there is some ionization, or electrical particles, surrounding it.)

To determine to what degree the space between the Earth

Fig. 7—A permanent, multiple satellite program with orbital vehicles serving as instruments of peace (open skies).

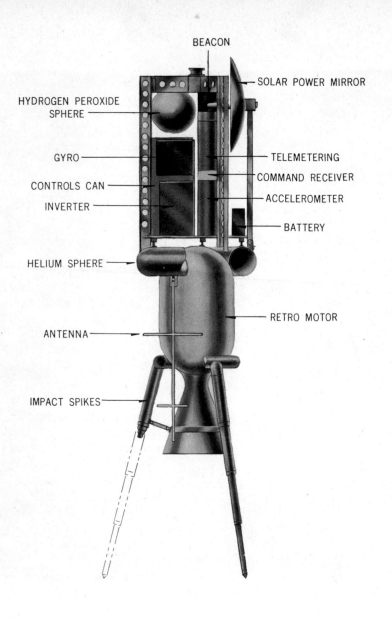

BEACON

SOLAR POWER MIRROR

HYDROGEN PEROXIDE
SPHERE

GYRO

CONTROLS CAN

INVERTER

TELEMETERING

COMMAND RECEIVER

ACCELEROMETER

BATTERY

HELIUM SPHERE

RETRO MOTOR

ANTENNA

IMPACT SPIKES

Fig. 8—Cutaway of lunar impact probe.

and Moon is tenanted by ionized gases, and if their presence is of permanent character.

Phase II. Landing an unmanned lunar probe on the Moon. The probe, as it falls toward the Moon, will be speeded up by the Moon's gravitational pull just as falling bodies are accelerated here on Earth. In order to prevent the probe from crashing and being completely destroyed on the lunar surface because of excessive speeds, retro-rockets (reverse rockets) are provided to break the fall, so that the probe can survive the impact.

Today, it is possible to build lunar data-gathering instrumentation, to be carried in the probe, that could survive the impact of a probe. A large mass of accurate and scientific information could be obtained in this way that certainly would not be possible via the probe pass or orbit techniques.

Such an unmanned lunar landing vehicle would also provide us with additional know-how in retro-landing control, guidance and propulsion—in preparation for the actual future manned landing.

Let us look for a moment at an artist's conception of our version of the first unmanned lunar attempt—Project Touchdown. (*See* Plate 3, following page 52.)

In the Project Touchdown drawing, three lunar space vehicles are shown, although only two appear readily apparent. Of these three vehicles, the two outer vehicles are "guidance drones" for the center or touchdown vehicle. The illustration shows the first guidance drone's impact on the Moon (in the lower right-hand corner), where the cold dark side of the Earth's own natural satellite merges with the warmer, light side. The vehicle which has already impacted provides one of the two "sensing" and guidance media for the control vehicle which has started its descent to the Moon's dead surface.

The other sensing vehicle (left center) is about to impact and has just emitted four different-colored flares, which can be spotted from the Earth. These flares help to provide additional guidance for the touchdown landing of the first unmanned vehicle in the center.

Unlike the sensing vehicles which plunge to destruction on

the lunar surface purely to provide visual markers, the landing vehicle is provided with a retro-rocket motor and impact spikes to limit the lunar impact to 100 *g's* or less.

A brief description of this first unmanned lunar impact vehicle follows. (*See* Fig. 8.) This final stage of a multistage vehicle will carry an instrumentation package on the top of its solid-propellant bottle. The complete impact vehicle will be 7 feet in height from the top of the instrument box to the bottom of the bottle's thrust chamber.

Just before landing and after burnout, three telescopic, dual-purpose, spiked landing legs will extend themselves and lock in a triangular position. Many of the impact spikes of the vehicle will be buried in the pumice and lava dust of the Moon on impact. After impact, the solar mirror which is used for power and is attached to the side of the instrument box will make it possible to send telemetered messages back to Earth via the television-type radar antennae on the other side of the vehicle. The instrument box houses gyroscopes, batteries, a beacon, telemetering, etc., among other electronic gear.

If the impact landing has been successful, there is a chance that many scientific messages containing information about lunar temperature, pressure, etc., can be relayed back to Earth.

The all-out attempt at a manned circumlunar flight would only be made after many unmanned lunar probes of all types have gathered sufficient information regarding the basic problem areas.

Phase III. The first manned lunar orbital mission—Project Moonmen. There has been much speculation about the first manned lunar vehicle that would transport man to our Moon and return him to Earth safely. The authors believe that the first lunar man-carrying vehicle will probably be boosted by a modified, multistage military vehicle. It will contain two passengers who will have a single mission—to leave the Earth—then orbit around the Moon once and return.

Many subsequent lunar trips would be made—first with two passengers and later with at least three passengers. These trips will probably be flown under the control and jurisdiction of a sovereign power like the United States or more likely an international body like the United Nations. Under this latter organization, this vehicle could conceivably have a multinational operating crew.

Phase IV. The first man on the Moon. After all necessary manned probe test flights are conducted, the final phase of the lunar program can be undertaken—a manned lunar landing.

The first manned lunar landing expedition will probably consist of three vehicles. Two of these three will be two-passenger space vehicles to act as observers and possibly cargo carriers. The third will be the three-passenger space vehicle that will carry a small Moon-landing "rocket personnel car" on its side. This small, nonstreamlined vehicle will perform the same function as dinghies for a ship at sea. So in our initial lunar landings, one or two humans will descend with the aid of the small rocket-propelled personnel carrier, while the mother ship and the observer ships continue in orbits around the Moon.

The personnel vehicles with their lightweight, cylindrical propellant tankage and structure will utilize retro-thrust rockets in landing on the Moon. These same rocket engines will later provide the necessary forward thrust to return the lunar explorers to the orbiting mother ship. As our Moon has only one-sixth the gravity of the Earth, not much thrust is required either in landing or departing.

One possible landing site for the first lunarians is the First North West Quadrant of the Moon's light side—probably on the circular Mare Serenitatis (or sea) which is approximately 325 miles in diameter. This "sea" is one of the more famous lunagraphic features—a favorite of the earthbound astronomers, who stare at it through their telescopes with visions and dreams of what it would really be like to land there.

Our landing site (10° W. 28° N.) is very close to Linné, the brightest and most studied spot on the whole lunar surface. This fascinating formation, which is thought to be a dome, is situated on Mare Serenitatis close to the mountain pass which separates the Haemus and the Caucasus Ranges. These latter mountains, with some of their peaks rising to over 19,000 feet, are an important range dividing the first landing site from the other "sea" close by, the Mare Imbrium.

The Haemus Mountains on the southern border of Mare Serenitatis are only 8,000 feet tall at their highest points, and merge with the foothills of the Apennines in the east. A particularly interesting lunagraphic feature is Menelaus, a brilliant crater, which is dazzlingly bright at full Moon. It is over 20 miles across and some 6,000 feet deep, with a small mountain in its center. This feature compares with Wizard Island in the center of Crater Lake in Oregon—without the cobalt-blue water surrounding it, of course.

Finally, to the southwest of our landing site (at 17° W. 22° N.) is the largest and most conspicuous crater on the Mare Serenitatis, Bessel, which is 12 miles wide and which possesses very bright walls. A curiously prominent bright ray passes through it from north to south, making this mysterious feature one of the first goals of lunar exploration.

Other lunagraphic features worth exploring on the first trip would include a visit to the Triesnecker Ariadaeus and the Hyginus Clefts, which are within a short walking distance to the south of our landing spot (4° W. 5° N.). Another remarkable system of clefts is found on the Mare Serenitatis, paralleling the mountains in a concentric pattern.

With all these varieties of lunagraphy to satisfy the appetites of the first lunar pioneers, it is no wonder that one of the brightest spots on the Moon—Linné—should be the center of attention as the first possible Moon target for man.

All that is needed to make a weekend holiday jaunt to this future vacation spot is the perfection of the rockets to get us there . . . and back.

The Moon Station

Once a successful landing has been accomplished, the problem of establishing a Moon station becomes paramount. As other experts have prognosticated the specifications of the Moon stations in great detail, we will only describe one type briefly here. (*See* Plate 4, following page 52.)

One possibility is to burrow into the mountainous walls or to dig caverns under the ground. This procedure would keep the transportation of building materials from the Earth at a minimum by utilizing the natural resources of the Moon instead. These underground chambers will be provided with an artificial atmosphere. They will also be air conditioned, and, with the aid of ultraviolet light, the health of the crews can be guaranteed for extended periods. The entrances will have air locks, similar to a submarine escape hatch. The station could be heated by either an atomic reactor using lunar minerals, or by solar mirror heaters. If there is no uranium for the reactor on the Moon, then other methods of extracting oxygen, nitrogen, hydrogen, and other gases from the rocks will provide the first lunar explorers with heat, air, and water . . . the basic necessities of life.

One possible great benefit to be derived from a lunar base will be the astronomical data relayed back to Earth by the members of the Moon station. Because there is no atmosphere on the Moon, the stars and the planets will be easier to observe at all times.

The Moon station can become the first real symbol of international co-operation working at its best. Supplying the lunar station will require that the larger nations contribute substantially, but the smaller nations could pool their efforts to do their part in a gigantic lunar lift.

Such a logistics problem as a lunar lift will require support and co-operation from all nations involved to ensure the success of the venture. Excellent precedent for such an undertaking has been the existence of multinational teams in the Antarctic during the International Geophysical Year, the joint Air Sea Rescue Squadrons in Europe today, or the Allied Air Sea Rescue Squadron that was located in Alipore, India, in World War II. This unique squadron, with a mission of mercy as its goal, was composed of rescue plane crews which often included British, Ameri-

can, French, Canadian, Australian, and Indian pilots, radio-
men, and navigators.

Similar international co-operative efforts could be established
in a comprehensive United Nations Moon Mission, which would
call on these past joint experiences during war and peacetime
to help iron out any international misunderstandings that might
occur in the planning and carrying out of such a project. Multinational representatives could and should man the first United
Nations lunar stations—as well as fly the transport rockets from
the Earth to these bases. All nations should be willing to contribute their share in this peaceful venture.

Moon Quest

The Moon is a symbol and a challenge. It will provide the
testing ground for man's actions during further explorations into
space.

If the Moon becomes a battleground for future wars of conquest between Earthmen, then our progress farther out into space
will probably be seriously hampered. If we become embroiled in
a cataclysmic war for the military control of the Moon, the argument that increased knowledge of military weaponry and space
missiles will speed up our going into space will no longer hold
true. So, philosophically speaking, the Moon becomes both the
means and the end in the next great step into space. The Moon
is a visible space symbol for all the peoples on the Earth to see,
a constant reminder that man's "Moon quest" offers a choice of
peace or war.

chapter 8

rocketry tomorrow

We believe that flight outside the atmosphere is a reality
that cannot and must not be minimized.
                    Brig. Gen. Hollingsworth F. Gregory
        Commander, Air Force Office of Scientific Research
        At the first U. S. Air Force Astronautical Symposium
                                        February 18, 1957

WE HAVE seen and are seeing the changes in Government policies and national attitudes regarding space flight that the world's comparatively low-performance, rocket-powered missiles are bringing about almost overnight. Although immediate changes are primarily military in nature, "rocketry tomorrow" will usher in a new era touching on all aspects of our daily living.

Recently, because of highly publicized rocket and satellite accomplishments, it has become apparent that future flights into the Universe are possible and that these flights will come about naturally as a direct result and progression from today's supermilitary missile and high-altitude rocket aircraft experiments. Yet, as complex and "ultimate" as these systems appear to be, there is no question that technological progress will show that these supersystems of today are only in the embryonic stage of development.

Just as our automobiles have increased in horsepower decade after decade, so the trend of flight history has continued to be toward faster and farther-reaching missiles. Through the normal process of growth, missile system refinements will most assuredly follow in many areas. In order to achieve greater speeds, one of the most pronounced areas of research is the development of better propulsion (engine) techniques. Axiomatically, it can be stated that "the future of rocketry and of space flight hinges predominantly on propulsion techniques."

Because the rocket will change our world as swiftly as the horseless carriage closed out the horse and buggy days, it becomes necessary that we understand rockets and their engines as well as we do our automobiles.

Thus, to better understand the "why" of today's rocket research, and "where" some of the future research efforts are being directed in the frantic search for better propulsion techniques, let us examine first the principle of operation and performance of some of the more conventional rocket engine systems that are available and others which have been proposed; then secondly, extrapolate from the present systems to the immediate future, examining the more exotic ideas that have been propounded; and finally, on the basis of the past and anticipated future propulsion performance try to answer several very timely questions posed by many; i.e., how fast and how far will man and his machines travel in the future and what will these machines look like?

The Principle of Rocket Engine Operation

First, in order to understand the principle of rocket propulsion, we must turn to Newton's Law of Motion, which states that every action has an equal and opposite reaction. This simple physical law describes uniquely the jet-reaction or rocket-propulsion principle. Figure 9 illustrates this principle applied to four of the better known, conventional types of chemical rocket-propulsion systems.

Operationally, a rocket engine utilizes a chemical fuel like gasoline and a chemical oxidizing agent to create thermal energy. (A rocket must carry its own oxygen since it operates outside the Earth's atmosphere.) The thermal energy, in turn, is converted to kinetic energy or jet velocity in the rocket nozzle.

In more basic terms, an oxidizer-fuel mixture is ignited in the engine's thrust chamber, producing flaming high-pressure combustion gases that roar out of the open end of the thrust chamber (engine nozzle) at very high jet exhaust speeds. This is the action. The reaction comes about from the tremendous force of the expanding gases on the closed end of the thrust chamber. This force produces the thrust or push that shoots the rocket upward and outward.

Engine Performance

When rocket performance is discussed, specific impulse and thrust are the most commonly used terms. These are the two basic rocket performance factors with which we should all become familiar. Specific impulse and thrust are to future space travelers what miles per gallon and horsepower are to today's motorists.

Specific impulse is defined as the engine thrust (push in pounds that the engine exerts on the missile) multiplied by the engine burning duration, divided by the quantity of propellant consumed.

As a classical example of specific impulse consider the performance of the V-2. With an engine thrust of 56,000 pounds, burning duration of 70 seconds and total propellant consumption of 19,000 pounds, the engine specific impulse (206 seconds) is found as follows:

$$\text{Specific Impulse} = \frac{56,000 \times 70}{19,000} = 206 \text{ seconds}$$

To demonstrate the social and economic importance of specific impulse and how it affects us directly, let us consider briefly the meaning of specific impulse as it applies to the field of transportation. First, assume that there is a requirement to build a transportation unit, such as a mail cargo or passenger rocket around the performance of the V-2, and that the specification calls for carrying 10,000 pounds of payload (cargo) between

Dallas, Texas and Salt Lake City, Utah, a distance of 1,000 miles.

A rocket-powered vehicle built to these specifications (10,000-pound payload) would probably have the following characteristics: takeoff gross weight, 92,000 pounds; thrust, 175,000 pounds; duration of powered flight, 85 seconds; cutoff altitude, 39 miles; apogee (maximum) altitude, 320 miles; and total flight time, 12¼ minutes to deliver 10,000 pounds of payload a distance of 1,000 miles. A comparable flight by airplane would require about two hours.

If a rocket cargo transport of this type were feasible today, its impact both economically and socially would be inestimable. Imagine rocketing at more than 4,000 miles per hour more than 100 miles above the Earth from New York to San Francisco, or across the Atlantic in a fraction of an hour. Or, on the other hand, visualize superfast cargo vehicles or mail carriers, coasting in their flight trajectories across oceans from continent to continent.

Superfast transportation systems of this type are definitely not science fiction but are concrete examples of things that man will make possible as he evolves into the Space Age. This becomes more and more apparent when one realizes that today's military rockets can deliver large destructive payloads halfway around the globe at speeds greater than 15,000 miles per hour. Peaceful applications of these same rocket vehicles promise to alter radically our future transportation systems as well as other aspects of the world we will be living in tomorrow.

The performance of the example cargo vehicle was based on the German V-2 (with a specific impulse of 206 seconds) which utilized alcohol as the fuel and liquid oxygen as the oxidizer, a combination which yields one of the highest specific impulses of the standard propellant combinations. Needless to say, this propellant combination is as good today as it was during the V-2 period. In fact, this propellant combination, with improved engine performance, is currently being used in some of the most advanced tactical weapons (IRBM and ICBM) and research (Vanguard) systems. Nevertheless, research is in progress and has been in progress since the end of World War II to develop higher energy propellant combinations.

During the early research stages, the development programs centered around not more than several oxidizers and fuels. Today the rocket propellant list consists of hundreds of propellant combinations.

In spite of great variations obtainable, improvements in specific impulse with our present standard propellant combinations are limited. This limitation follows from the fact that today's propellants, consisting of the elements hydrogen, carbon, oxygen, or nitrogen produce combustion products which disassociate (separate) rapidly above 4,000 degrees Fahrenheit. Disassociation of these combustion products results in a loss in rocket jet exhaust velocity. Jet exhaust energy losses and the inability of known metals to withstand high temperatures, in the final analysis, limit the specific impulse obtainable from standard chemical rocket propellants to approximately 250 seconds.

In practice, therefore, single-stage missiles utilizing the standard chemical propellant combination, can, at best, achieve a final velocity of approximately 8,000 to 10,000 miles per hour. The missions that such missiles can perform are obviously limited; because, for example, the Earth's escape velocity is approximately 25,000 miles per hour. Thus, additional solutions must be investigated and applied in order to overcome this barrier.

At present we have two temporary remedies—*staging* and *orbital refueling*—to aid us in our pioneer steps into space with today's standard chemical propellants.

Staging and Orbital Refueling

The theoretical aspects of staging to overcome the final velocity problem were well understood long before World War II. Fundamentally, staging consists of placing a complete but small rocket in the nose of a larger rocket. The large rocket, commonly referred to as the booster, fires first. When the booster has exhausted its propellants and achieved peak velocity, it is separated from the smaller rocket—the second stage. The second stage, going along for the ride, inherits the booster's velocity. After separation from the booster stage, the second stage fires its rocket and proceeds to add its own speed to that given it by the booster. In this manner, a two-stage rocket more than doubles the final velocity obtainable with a single-stage rocket. To achieve still higher final velocities one can utilize three, four, and sometimes even more stages. The disadvantage of multistage rockets is that each stage must be enormously larger than the stage it boosts. Therefore, to place extremely large payloads into space requires multistage rockets many times heavier than our largest modern bombers.

In order to overcome the attendant size problem (which is brought about by the use of staging) for large payload space missions, the second "remedy" of orbital refueling can be used. Orbital refueling, in conjunction with staging in practice, would be the same as our flight refueling of large modern bombers. Briefly, the orbital refueling technique proposes to split up a particular mission into phases—working on the principle that it is easier to transport a load of bricks a few at a time than to try to carry all of them all the way at one time.

High-Thrust Engines

Thus, it is possible with today's chemical propellants, along with staging and orbital refueling, to carry moderate payloads; i.e., man and/or his instruments, to the Moon and beyond. However, in order to carry extremely large payloads on similar missions, very high-thrust booster engines are required. Our need for a single high-thrust rocket engine (for example, a minimum of 1,000,000 pounds thrust) is therefore foreseeable and necessary.

There are two ways to achieve this initial high-thrust boost—by using clusters of small-thrust engines or developing a single large-thrust engine. Today, the largest single rocket engine in the United States is reported to be on the order of 150,000 pounds thrust. Clusters of this basic engine have been considered for various applications. The growth in engine-thrust levels taken from unclassified sources since the advent of modern rocketry is depicted in Figure 10.

With our current rate of thrust-level growth extrapolated (indicated by the dash lines) into the immediate future, it can be seen that in the course of normal development, a 1,000,000-pound-thrust engine should be available by 1962. Unfortunately, nowhere in American unclassified sources is a development engine of this thrust level mentioned. On the other hand, it has been reported from authoritative sources that the Russians are developing a single-thrust chamber of 820,000 pounds thrust.

Constructively, the authors recommend that this area be given a long hard look. It is our opinion that a high-thrust-level engine development program should be initiated within the next fiscal year. The primary aim of this program should be to maintain in constant development at least three high-thrust, state-of-the-art development engines. The thrust level of these engines should be a least five to ten years in advance of requirements, and at least one engine should be designed to use a storable semi-permanent propellant system (as opposed to liquid oxygen which boils away quickly).

High-Energy Chemical Propellants

Along with a long view of large-thrust engine development programs, added emphasis should be placed on the development of high-energy chemical propellant systems, as well as the so-called exotic propulsion systems to be discussed later.

The high-energy chemical propellant systems, such as fluorine-hydrazine, are basically the same as the standard systems, except that the high-energy systems yield much higher engine specific impulse; i.e., on the order of 300 seconds as compared to 250 seconds for the standard system.

The effects of high-energy propellants on missile design and performance are twofold. First, from a design standpoint for a particular mission, the use of high-energy propellants will reduce the size of a single-stage vehicle appreciably, or reduce the number of stages required for a multistage vehicle as compared to one using conventional propellants. Secondly, from a performance standpoint, the use of high-energy propellants will result in substantially greater payloads of instruments, men, or cargo.

As an additional illustration of the effects of specific impulse on vehicle design, let us consider our previous cargo vehicle requirements—delivery of a 10,000-pound payload 1,000 miles.

Designing the vehicle around the high-energy propellant combination of fluorine-hydrazine (specific impulse—300 seconds), we now find the redesigned vehicle would have a takeoff gross weight of 31,000 pounds as compared to 92,000 pounds for the original vehicle designed around V-2 performance. Furthermore, if we want to design a vehicle with a takeoff gross weight of 92,000 pounds, as in the V-2 example, then, by the use of fluorine-hydrazine propellants, the payload-carrying capability of this vehicle would be increased from the initial 10,000 pounds to approximately 30,000 pounds.

Most important, however, is the fact that the specific impulse obtainable from the high-energy chemical propellants is inadequate and on the very low side of the specific impulse spectrum. For rocketry to be competitive with other types of jet-propulsion devices, a specific impulse on the order of 3,500 to 5,000 seconds is required. This would position rocket propulsion on a par with today's jet engines and make rocket passenger and cargo transports feasible.

However, in order to make space flights to the planets practical on a large scale, specific impulse greater than 5,000 seconds should be available. It is interesting to note at this point that the ultimate jet velocity—the speed of light, 186,000 miles per second—is attainable from a photon rocket, which theoretically can deliver a specific impulse of 30,500,000 seconds.

Figure 11 illustrates the improvement in specific impulse that has been achieved in the last fifty years. Of special interest to us is the extrapolation of today's performance to the future, the year A.D. 2000, at the time when most of our children will be living their adult lives. It can be seen that if the growth of specific impulse continues in the established trend, then, by the year A.D. 2000, system performance will be approaching 10,000 seconds. However, a 10,000-seconds specific impulse will not be achieved in one step. The attainment of this performance will be gradual and probably require thirty to forty years.

For the next generation of rocket engines and sequentially the next achievable level in the specific impulse spectrum, we must look beyond chemical reaction for our source of energy. It is most generally agreed that this source will be the atom.

Nuclear Propulsion

There are two promising techniques which may someday harness the energy of the atom for rocket propulsion. These are nuclear fusion and nuclear fission. Both the fusion reactor and the fission reactor utilize atomic energy.

What is fusion? Fusion takes place when the nuclei of the lightest elements such as heavy hydrogen or tritium fuse and form heavier nuclei. Fusion or thermonuclear reaction is what occurs when a hydrogen bomb is detonated. This same process is occurring in the core of the Sun and the distant stars.

What is fission? Fission takes place when nuclei of the heaviest elements such as uranium or thorium split into lighter fragments. Fission reaction is what occurs when an atomic bomb is set off, or what takes place in our new electrical atomic powerplants.

In both processes, fusion and fission, energy is produced by the direct conversion of mass into energy. One of these processes—fusion—appears to be more promising, however.

What makes fusion more desirable than fission for power reactor purposes? First, if a controlled thermonuclear power station could be built, the fusion reactor will probably produce energy directly in the form of an electric current, which is a highly efficient process and a desirable form of power conversion for rocket engine applications. Secondly, it would mean that sea water could be used to provide hydrogen as fuel for these applications. The fuel supply would be unlimited. It has been estimated by some scientists that this form of power can sustain one thousand times the current world's power requirements for billions of years.

How safe is fusion? If controlled thermonuclear reaction is achieved, it would mean an end to the common hazards of dangerous radiation now being experienced with fission reactors. The reaction products of the fusion process do not emit dangerous gamma rays.

What are the problem areas of fusion? As attractive as this energy source is, there are outstanding technological problems which have temporarily stymied its development. One of the most fundamental problems is that we are unable to contain ("box in") the reactants during the fusion process because of the very high temperature required (180,000,000 degrees Fahrenheit) to fuse the atoms of light elements.

When will fusion be available? Currently, researchers are at work in the United States, England, and Russia, trying to produce controlled fusion reaction. It has been estimated by some scientists that fusion power stations will be built within fifteen to twenty-five years.

The fusion reactor rocket engine will follow closely on the heels of the development of an industrial fusion reactor, as is currently taking place with the fission reactor.

The fission reactor, of which there are several types, has been successfully developed for industrial-type applications. In its industrial form, the fission reactor is unsuitable for flight applications. However, modifications of this basic reactor are underway to extend its utility from industrial uses to aircraft and rocket propulsion.

In its initial form, the nuclear rocket will probably utilize the heat produced by nuclear fission to heat and vaporize a fluid to some high temperature. The resulting high-temperature gases will then be expanded through a nozzle similar to the chemical rocket. The specific impulse delivered by a nuclear rocket in this manner is very impressive compared to the conventional energy rocket. For example, hydrogen heated by the nuclear reactor to 4,000 degrees Fahrenheit will produce a specific impulse better than 860 seconds, which more than doubles that obtainable from chemical reaction.

With these large amounts of energy available in the atom (equivalent to the power of gasoline multiplied by 3,000,000, or, expressed in another form, a small quantity of uranium contains, theoretically, enough power to propel a spaceship to Mars), one might wonder why the Atomic Age did not usher in space flight on a large scale immediately.

The answer is basic. First, in order to achieve high specific impulse with a nuclear engine, high-temperature gases are required. However, just as with the chemical engine rocket, the nuclear engine is limited, because materials cannot withstand the desired high temperatures. Secondly, the radiation hazard to men and materials from alpha particles, gamma rays, and neutrons requires that extremely heavy shielding be provided for protection. Adequate shielding requirements make nuclear engines impractical from an engine weight standpoint. And, thirdly, similar to our modern liquid rocket missiles, the nuclear fission engine also requires a working fluid which results in an elaborate system of tanks, valves, and pumps, etc.

Taking these factors into consideration, a nuclear-powered space vehicle becomes an extremely large and complex system. Figure 12 is an artist's conception of a nuclear space vehicle.

Manned Nuclear Space Vehicles

With all its apparent limitations, a nuclear rocket is expected to be available within the next few years, capable of providing a specific impulse range between 400 and 900 seconds, depending on the working fluid. (For example: water, ammonia, or hydrogen, etc.)

Furthermore, although the power of the atom is recognized as one of the more important immediate sources of energy for large-thrust booster engines, its ultimate applications will be realized in the future at a time when its energy will be used for flight among the planets and stars. The nuclear rocket engine, which will propel these future spaceships, might also be removed and installed as an industrial power source on distant celestial bodies. The additional humanitarian benefits that will be derived from a successful development of a practical reactor stagger the imagination.

The chemical and the nuclear fission propulsion systems discussed up to this point are considered "conventional" and refer to applications of the launch boost type. However, there are many other types of propulsion techniques that have been considered for rocket propulsion from time to time. Several of the better known systems are free radicals, arc heating, solar power, antigravity, ion, and photon. Some of these systems are ideally suited for boost launch applications, while still others are only applicable for "deep" space flights. Regardless of their application, some are practical and others are just interesting conversational pieces and mathematical exercises at this time. All propulsion systems of this type are today considered to be in the "exotic" family of propulsion systems.

Ion Propulsion

Probably the "exotic" propulsion system of immediate importance and one which holds the greatest promise for "deep" space flight is the ion system.

The inherent characteristics of an ion system make its application ideally suitable for spaceship navigation corrections, transfer between satellite orbits, or for powering flights within and beyond our Solar System. The ion system is operationally unique in that it is under power for long durations of time, and, during these periods, the thrust exerted and vehicle accelerations always remain small. High-thrust and high-acceleration booster systems, on the other hand, normally are under power for less than three minutes.

An ion is defined as an atom or molecule that is electrically unbalanced due to a gain or loss of one or more electrons. Therefore, depending on the source (material used), the resulting particle can have either a positive or negative charge.

Ion energy can be manifested in two types of ion-propulsion

systems—recombination or the accelerated ion. Rocket exhaust velocities obtainable from an ion recombination process are small as compared to the accelerated ion system which theoretically can achieve velocities approaching the speed of light. Therefore, because of the relative energy levels of the two systems, the accelerated ion is the system that is receiving the greatest amount of consideration for space-flight applications.

The accelerated ion rocket system receives its thrust from the reaction of accelerated (directed) beams of charged ions. Acceleration of the charged ions is achieved by means of an electric field. The final velocity of the ion can theoretically approach the speed of light. To obtain high ionic velocities, high-energy accelerators on the order of hundreds of millions of volts must be utilized.

Successful development of an ion-propulsion system is contingent upon developing a reliable source for creating ions as well as developing an electrical power source for ion acceleration. It has been prognosticated by many rocket experts that the first prototype ion rocket will probably be available within twenty-five years.

Rocketry Reprise

We have briefly examined the direction and scope of rocketry tomorrow through the sequence of the developments in the state-of-the-art that will probably occur. Progress in conventional chemical and high-energy chemical propulsion; the necessity of staging; orbital refueling; high-thrust engines; and, finally, the next generation of rocket systems, the nuclear and ion engines, were discussed.

The foregoing analysis shows that man definitely has a future potential in extending himself into space through advances in rocketry. Many of the advances noted herein will come as a consequence of previous developments.

The curves we have plotted on a 100-year development of rocketry into the future, show, among other facts, that man will be traveling at least 50,000 miles per hour in the year A.D. 2000

(*See* Fig. 13), and his instruments up to 150,000 miles per hour. (*See* Fig. 14.) It is interesting to note that the 100-year curve of the manned-flight spectrum follows a straighter and more normal learning path than the unmanned one. One reason for this apparent slower advance is the necessity of more adequate safeguards for the human passengers than are necessary for the instruments alone.

However, we should like to point out that these curves do not take into consideration accelerations in learning, know-how, or major breakthroughs in the state-of-the-art in rocketry. They are based on the past and present developments only, and thus give us a rational pattern for extending our predictions into the future. We believe that this method at best will give us very conservative estimates of where we are going when we extrapolate our growth potential on how fast and how far man and his machines will travel into space in the future.

Thus by understanding the fundamentals of rocketry and its anticipated pattern of chronological growth, we will be better prepared to adjust and accept the consequences resulting from our future spatial penetrations.

But probably the most important results of a close analysis of "rocketry tomorrow" is the realization that we *can* and we *will* be traveling faster and farther into space and in orbits around the Earth. These factors lead us to the inevitable conclusion that man will need to develop a parallel program for the international control of space.

Furthermore, because rocketry advances have made it possible to cut across national boundaries, the United Nations should immediately consider the consequences of the present and future results of these new technological capabilities. In several of the chapters that follow, there are presented a series of steps which may be used in establishing a workable program for the international control of space. Meanwhile, the alternative approach to the control of space on a national level will be examined in the next chapter.

chapter 9

the need for space doctrine

In the long haul our safety as a nation may depend upon
our achieving space superiority. . . . Several decades from
now the important battles may not be sea battles or air
battles, but space battles. . . . We should be spending a
certain fraction of our national resources to insure that
we do not lag in obtaining space supremacy.

Maj. Gen. Bernard A. Schriever
Commander, Ballistic Missile Division
U. S. Air Force

ATTAINMENT of the ability of man to travel in
outer space may take a few years, but the time for contempla-
tion of consequences of manned space travel has arrived. Men
and women must be mentally prepared for the revolutionary
space experiences now in prospect, including an understanding
of some of the geopolitical-military implications of space doctrine. Time is growing short. Gil Robb Wilson, the prominent
exponent of airpower, stated recently that he had no fear that
the United States would perfect satellites and missiles, but he
did fear that it might not take the lead in providing the proper
employment concepts to use them.

Like the western frontier in America in the latter part of the
19th century, we have discovered a new frontier with similar
conditions. Like the settlers in the Old West who lost their
stakes and claims when they did not maintain the power to
protect those claims, the United States is seeking to exert its
claim in space and to keep its control out of the absolute hands

of potential enemies who would exploit space for their own
ruthless ends.

In November, 1957, Gen. Thomas D. White, Chief of Staff
of the United States Air Force, at long last stated a broad out-
line of space doctrine when he said, ". . . whoever has the capability to control the air is in a position to exert control over
the land and seas beneath. I feel that in the future whoever
has the capability to control space will likewise possess the capability to exert control of the surface of the earth. . . .

"In speaking of the control of air and the control of space,
I want to stress that there is no division, per se, between air
and space. Air and space are an indivisible field of operations.

"Ninety-nine percent of the earth's atmosphere lies within 20
miles of the surface of the earth. It is quite obvious that we cannot control the air up to 20 miles above the earth's surface and
relinquish control of space above that altitude . . . and still survive."

Now that man has broken through the restricting envelope
surrounding the Earth, he will, from a military realm, have to
assure himself that his nation's air space beneath him is controlled and adequately protected. Thus, a foundation for the
understanding and realization of space doctrine is dependent
on the degree of airpower control in the atmosphere below the
space frontier. By military *spacepower*, then, we mean "the ability of a nation or group of nations to exert their will via the
space medium," which parallels airpower's definition of the
"ability of a nation to exert its will via the *air* medium." These
two conjunctive types of power should never be thought of sep-
arately, but always as two parts of the whole. Space vehicles
will thus carry man (or his controlled electronic instruments at
first) into the unknown altitude areas where new political, economic, social, and military problems will be accrued to him on
Earth as a result of his conquest of space.

Changes Wrought by the Conquest of Space

Of the many changes in man's thinking regarding the use and control of space, the most obvious and significant is the *obliteration of national air boundaries*.

Due to the limited altitudes of present-day air vehicles, powerful military nations can control their air space as a privileged sanctuary in peacetime—regarded as inviolate as their homeland below—according to the present rules of international law. The advent of space satellites, guided missiles, and spaceships has led to a revolution in national air sovereignty.

With the launching of the first Earth satellite, a new era has begun—the end of national control over upper air space. Space is truly international, no matter how one divides it. Any point at 200, 300, or 1,000 miles up is probably dominating some or all of two or more nations simultaneously, and this fact complicates the problems between nations regarding the sovereignty of their former aerial domains.

The elimination of national air and space boundaries would mean that President Eisenhower will eventually win a *fait accompli* victory for his open-skies policy, whether or not other nations accept this fact by signatures on diplomatic documents giving open-skies permission. Now that the first satellites have been launched, it is only a matter of time before powerful aerial cameras will be perfected to transmit electronically televised pictures of formerly inaccessible territory and installations back to Earth. Constant inspection of countries, cities, and bodies of water can be maintained by satellites, and potentially set our "warning bells ringing" on any future enemy buildup leading to another Pearl Harbor-type attack.

In a June, 1956, issue of *Life*, Charles J. V. Murphy, one of the nation's foremost aviation writers, had this to say about satellites: "An effective space platform, equipped with cameras and telemetering devices, would provide either the Russians or ourselves with a means of continuous surveillance of each other's industrial and missile deployments—crucial intelligence in a period when nations will have power to obliterate their enemies."

General Clarence S. Irvine told the Johnson committee in December, 1957, that the U. S. Air Force had been working for a long time on a program for a reconnaissance satellite, and that it now has cameras capable of taking pictures of the earth from a satellite in orbit. "This is the first step towards peace," he said.

At increasing distances from the Earth, consistent with advances in surveillance techniques, more of the Earth's surface can be dominated by any single reconnaissance space vehicle, and the former aerial sovereign safety zones on Earth will be all but eliminated. Although it will be possible to hide some missile-launching sites underground, thus making it difficult to detect small objects from the "Big Brother" type reconnaissance satellites, the cameras nevertheless can accomplish much.

One other fact that will make for the obliteration of national air boundaries is the necessity of establishing widely dispersed, international ground-control nets to guarantee that space vehicles reach the proper altitudes for operation. While flying over foreign territory, a space vehicle must, in some cases, rely on ground-control stations in that country to gain the proper altitude. Thus, a handful of the larger territorial nations on Earth have it within their power to hamper other nations' attempts to perform high-altitude flying, if they try to retain their air space as a sovereign entity.

Military Control of Space

Current U. S. Air Force doctrine is based on the theory of control of the air. Since the degree of control by the United States and its allied air forces is relative at any given moment, several factors become apparent when we extend this theory to control of space. Such space control would deny to an enemy his objectives—which is the main aim of spacepower.

The greater the distance from the Earth, the more air space there is to control. This assumption leads one to the belief that as man ascends out of the atmosphere and into space, it will become more difficult for him to control absolutely the significant portions of the air, ocean, and space between him and the

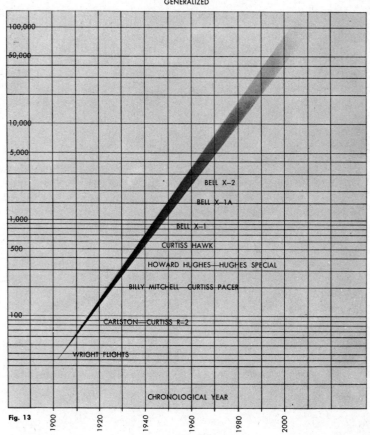

ONE-HUNDRED-YEAR PROGRESS
MANNED FLIGHT SPECTRUM
GENERALIZED

Fig. 13

Plate 4—Lunar exploration party leaving Linné settlement.

Earth. This assumption, when extended to its logical conclusion, would lead one to believe that to retain comparative control of both the air and space, those nations trying for such control would have to increase their air and space vehicles numerically or qualitatively in direct proportion to the additional miles of distance reached. They would also have to provide for complete surveillance and countermeasures.

The characteristics of vertical employment is one of the advantages of airpower (and military spacepower) over land- or water-borne weapons of war. The extended application of this characteristic to higher altitudes multiplies the problem of control over the dominions of outer space and the Earth's atmosphere. But one fact is clear: the nation that masters speed and distance, coupled with staying power, will be in a position to dominate the world, even though the problems and areas of control become more difficult in scope.

Such a nation could also guarantee better freedom of flight in the air space, although fixing set frontiers in the layers and spheres of the atmosphere and space would be a big problem.

The greater the distance reached, the greater the potential degree of control. Conversely, to offset the disadvantage posed by larger distances—the problem of more space to control in all directions—is the advantage of being on top. Imagine standing on the summit of Mount Everest with all the rest of the known Earth's crust below you!

Knowledge that other nations have not gone out so far as you have, gives the "outer" nation a feeling of security that no others can have—a command control over the Earth. On this point Stefan T. Possony and Leslie Rosenzweig in a significant article entitled, "The Geography of the Air," published in *The Annals of The American Academy of Political and Social Science* for May, 1955, wrote: "As man reaches upwards to the outer atmosphere, new political problems arise, the nature of which we are as yet unable to grasp. Heretofore the relations between nations took place on what in practice was a plane. During the time of low-altitude flying, the relations between nations and military forces were determined by the geometry of a spheroid's curved surface. This period of close-to-the-ground flying was, and still is, characterized by the 'polar concept.' Henceforth, international relations will be geared to the more difficult geometry of the interior of a large spheroid enveloping as its core a smaller and impenetrable spheroid, the earth. But even more confusing, the radius of the outer spheroid—symbolizing the aeropause or the altitude which man has attained at any given time—is expanding. The technologically most advanced nation will operate within the highest aeropause, while the spheroids circumscribing the aerial capabilities of the more backward nations will have shorter radii. Hence, in the future, the geometry of power will be described by several enveloping spheroids of different sizes. It will be a far cry from the geometry of the battles of Yorktown and Bastogne, or even from the aerial battles of World War II. Truly, a new *Weltbild* is emerging."

The Strategic and Tactical Importance of Space Vehicles

Translated into simple language, this statement means that those nations that can successfully launch and maintain the greatest number of manned and unmanned satellites in space will have further opportunities to exert their will in the air and space medium.

This fact makes the perfection of long-range, nuclear-powered air and space vehicles a significant step forward in winning the air and space battle for control in peace or war. The prolongation of flight around the Earth by manned nuclear air and space vehicles will help to make possible a continuing air-space sentinel system, not possible heretofore. The perfection of manned air and space vehicles which are nuclear or other powered will make control more feasible as a nation's nuclear-powered capability increases.

Such a sustaining ability at the greatest distance and with the greatest speed will enable the nation that possesses these characteristics to exert all five of the fundamental effects which a military force of that nation would be able to produce on other nations in varying degrees. These effects in order are: (1) persuasion (2) neutralization, (3) denial, (4) destruction, and (5) capture. Space doctrine, when applied, would make the first three of these five effects particularly effective on those nations to whom they are aimed. The latter two effects—destruction and capture—need never be exerted or carried out if the first three are applied judiciously by the nation or nations exerting them.

The counterspace battle requires that an enemy be hit or killed primarily in space and not on the ground. This fact stems from the previous assumption that perpetually flying, nuclear-powered space vehicles would have to be knocked out somewhere in space rather than at their launch sites. This is essential because ground nuclear wars or nuclear bombs dropped from space on ground targets are no longer feasible from a humanitarian or a survival standpoint. The requirement to stop such enemy vehicles in the air space differs from the current doctrine of stopping potential aggressors on the ground before they can launch an attack. As this type of vehicle is not a land-oriented vehicle, there is one desirable place where it should be destroyed, and that is in its natural habitat—air space. To concentrate on finding an enemy's space-launching sites on land would be well-nigh impossible after hostilities had started (unless one was thinking of a preventive war). Even then, the main threat which would already be airborne and space-borne could not be overlooked.

Since more potential vehicles of destruction will be in flight rather than at their launching sites at the outbreak of hostilities between any two or more major Earth nations, an added burden will be put on the defender nation. In some respects, it is an almost *impossible* task for a nation to try to defend itself against a multitude of enemy long-range missiles and military satellites that are constantly whirling around the Earth in orbit. These combat space weapons, awaiting the moment when they are to be simultaneously redirected down through the atmosphere to wipe out some unfriendly nation, pose a threat which at the moment defies man's imagination to fabricate a workable defense. At present, antimissile missile plans, such as the U. S. Air Force's Wizard Project and the Army's Nike-Zeus anti-ICBM program, are still on the drawing boards. It is reliably estimated that the United States is at least four years away from an operational antimissile missile.

Some Defensive Aspects of Space Doctrine

Although most military spacepower adherents consider mainly the offensive function of this new form of military power, we must not let ourselves become blinded by this aspect to the detriment of the important defensive functions. With the United States putting most of "her eggs in the offensive airpower (Strategic Air Command) basket" after World War II, it can truly be said that the nation has done so at the expense of its defensive effort, particularly its passive civilian defense.

When we speak of a defensive space doctrine, we should not limit our thinking to antimissile missiles, Distant Early Warning (DEW) Lines, and Texas Tower picket stations (permanent water-fixed platforms), or to the equally significant underground dispersal shelters to protect the population from the possibility of deadly thermonuclear consequences. The complacency among Americans over the feeble efforts that had been made before sputnik to awaken the public to the needs of a well-planned and urgent Civil Defense Program was shattered with the fears and fright that arose after October 4, 1957.

Burrowing underground as the Swedes have been doing for the past several years appears to be an alternative and/or complementary approach to an all-out ICBM-IRBM program. Placing factories, hangars, docks, and businesses underground, in addition to the conventional personnel shelters, is a tremendous undertaking both in time, money, and manpower. Another alternative to pursue in this vital area is elaborated upon in Chapters 12 and 13—with the thesis that United Nations control of space will erase the fear complex, which is the basis of the "billion dollar burrowing underground" Civil Defense Program. Instead of going down, why not go out?

The Space Doctrine Challenge

In one sense, we find ourselves today on the threshold of space, in a similar state as that of the hunter on a safari who has reached the edge of a dense jungle. The size and number of his weapons will determine how far into the jungle he can penetrate and still retain hopes of returning safely to civilization. He knows he cannot go too far if he does not possess the implements to fight his way out—alive.

We need to coin a valid space doctrine to keep the myriad space satellites, rocketships, intercontinental missiles, and space stations from getting out of control. Such a doctrine, coined jointly by *military, political, university,* and *missile industry* experts, is necessary to provide a secure foundation for space doctrine in the future, and to aid us in understanding the technologically complex struggle for control of the Earth's air and the space beyond. The formulation of this doctrine should be monitored by United Nations representatives from each nation. The visionaries in the advanced-design sections of leading missile and aircraft industries can make many valuable suggestions to the military planners who are grappling with the never-ending problems of future strategies. With the added knowledge of *where* the United States is going and *how,* the key advanced-design thinkers in the space-flight industries can provide valuable leadership in this area. As the space revolution gathers momentum, the people are challenged, as never before, to face up to the tasks of a new international spacepower and to learn to cope with its changing nature. The hopes and fears of our civilization and of the Universe are tied to the necessity of such an understanding *now.*

Space flight should help to bring the world closer together—rather than divide it. True space flight to the planets (and the stars) will come only after the world is united and the threat of war is removed. This is the ultimate challenge to mankind: that spacepower may be used for peaceful purposes.

chapter 10

who owns space?

We must work for . . . mutual control of the outer space
missile and the earth satellite.
                        President Dwight D. Eisenhower
                        State of the Union message
                        to Congress—January 10, 1957

WHO owns space?" Before we answer this question, let us ask, "Where does national sovereignty end?" "Where does space begin?" In earlier times on this Earth, the seaward limits of national sovereignty were determined by the "cannon shot" rule, with the three-mile limit being the maximum range of the cannons of the era. This rule applied horizontally outward from the borders of a country. Vertically, however, the earliest accepted doctrine of the ownership of air space stemmed from English common law. The doctrine of unlimited ownership upward over the land below was known as *Cujus est solum ejus est usque ad cœlum* or "Whose is the soil, his it is up to the sky."

From Roman times to the advent of air travel, the landowner, be he a farmer, a baron, a king of a nation, had no inherent limitations on the use of space over his land, and at the same time he could prevent others from interfering with it.

Since aviation came into its own during the first half of the 20th century, a set of rules and agreements have been formulated by the various nations reversing the *cujus est solum* doctrine. Most of the restrictions and limitations over the use of air space were agreed to by the nations in concert with the

International Civil Aviation Organization (ICAO), acting as the monitoring agency for conflicts.

But now the sputniks and outer-space missiles have jolted these concepts of sacred national air-space sovereignty that have been the accepted rules of air law for the second quarter of the 20th century.

Although the ICAO outlaws pilotless flights over the territory of other states without special authority, it is to be noted that the Soviet Union is not a party to that convention. However, all the sixty-four participating nations in the International Geophysical Year of 1957–58 mutually agreed to tolerate all flights of peaceful scientific Earth satellites over their territories.

This agreement, approved by the scientific delegations from the IGY nations, represents an important step toward the ultimate general acceptance of the international character of the regions of contiguous space beyond the air we breathe.

Government attorneys confirm that, prior to the White House announcement on July 27, 1955, that the United States would launch a satellite during the International Geophysical Year, special conferences on international law were held to discuss some of the more serious legal problems of free space, notably the upward extent of national sovereignty. It is felt that President Eisenhower did not make his historic announcement until after he had received the green light that no established principles of international law would be violated.

Let us look briefly at status and development of international air law, which led up to the President's satellite announcement.

The Historical Background for Present Theories of Space Law

In 1910, mainly because the French were worried about German balloons drifting over French territory, the International Air Navigation Conference was held in Paris. Out of the conference came a severe difference of opinion of the question of whether flight should be free or subject to control of nations over which pilots flew. Although no agreement was reached, the group in favor of control appeared to have won its point.

Some nine years later, at a similar convention on the Regulation of Aerial Navigation held in Paris, not only did the participating nations assert their sovereignty over the "air space" above them, but they insisted that all aircraft have a nationality; i.e., those aircraft having atmospheric support. Although its representatives attended the 1919 convention, the United States never ratified the pact.

The U. S. Congress, by the Air Commerce Act of 1926, finally asserted exclusive national sovereignty for the United States in the air space above it, and at the same time defined aircraft "as any contrivance now known or hereafter invented, used or designed for navigation or flight in the air."

The latest international meeting was the Chicago Convention on International Civil Aviation held in 1944. Most nations, including the United States, are parties to it, but the Soviet Union and China, along with the other Communist nations, do not belong. The significant portion of the Chicago pact says that: "The contracting States recognize that every state has complete and exclusive sovereignty of the airspace above its territory." Although aircraft are given the attributes of nationality by the Chicago Convention, neither the term "air space" nor "aircraft" is defined in the treaty.

Today, there are *no* international agreements that specifically limit, define, or signify the ownership of outer-space instrumentalities. This lack of agreement (except on the IGY sputniks) is the major challenge today to those persons and nations sincerely interested in compiling an accepted set of space law principles.

Is the space, between 250- to 850-mile altitude of the elliptical orbit of the first sputniks, free space? No responsible world authority seems to know the answer, because the basic question of "How high is up?" has never been settled. Although Willy Ley, the noted rocket expert, feels that space begins at 100 miles above the Earth's surface, the question still remains: "Whose space?"

With the recent announcements of the successful launchings of the first Earth satellites, and tests of Soviet and American IRBM's and ICBM's, it is not too early to contemplate the foundation of space law as to the future ownership and utilization of space.

A noted international lawyer, C. Wilfred Jenks of Great Britain, recently summed up the imperative timeliness for seriously promulgating a set of space rules and codifying them into an acceptable body of space law that will be mutually accepted by all nations. "It is not premature," he wrote, "for international lawyers to give some preliminary consideration to the problems which will confront them as a matter of urgency if the current efforts of scientists and engineers specializing in astronautics and electronics should suddenly achieve a dramatic success comparable in the range and speed of its repercussions to the explosion of the first atomic bomb. . . .

"While it is healthy," he continued, "that the evolution of the law should follow rather than anticipate that of life, there are circumstances in which the possibility of developing the law on sound principles depends primarily on initiative being taken in the matter before de-facto situations have crystallized too far. The exploration and exploitation of space may proceed as slowly as the course of polar exploration or the conquest of Everest; they may however, develop as rapidly as the utilization of atomic energy, or of rocket propulsion. It is wise to be prepared for any eventuality."

With technology beating on the door of space, a search for a rational and acceptable space control theory is essential to help ensure the survival of civilization.

Five Leading Theories of Space Control

In the past few years, several international lawyers of note have taken an interest in space law in its embryonic state and have written monographs or read papers on the subject at recent gatherings of lawyers and rocketeers. Their theses have appeared in various learned journals, such as: *Missiles and Rockets, Jet*

Propulsion, The Journal of Air Law and Commerce, The Harvard Law Review, The Nation's Business, and the *International and Comparative Law Quarterly.* Excerpts and briefs of five of the leading theories will be analyzed in an ascending space control sequence. (*See* Fig. 17.)

1. Schachter Air Space Theory

Oscar Schachter, an English international lawyer and Director of the General Legal Division of the United Nations, has fathered the Air Space Theory, which is presently adhered to by many U. S. Government experts, as it is the most expedient theory politically. Schachter's theory holds that national sovereignty upward is limited to navigable air space, with the limit of sovereign control being the ceilings of the highest "lift" of present manned aircraft (20 miles) and reaching up to a maximum of 40 miles tomorrow.

This doctrine has the advantages of being the easiest to understand and of possessing some legal precedents. This latter fact is imbedded in the present multilateral air treaty agreed to by forty-nine nations at the Chicago Convention of 1944. Although this treaty is adhered to by most of the civilized world in granting exclusive state sovereignty to air space over national territories, it has the flaw of not defining the term "air space," which makes a definitive legal interpretation cloudy. Because of this semantic confusion, there is no general agreement of a 20-mile or 40-mile height limit of sovereign control by the leading nations.

The fault with this theory is that it lacks realism, since sovereign nations today do about what they please, except where they enter into mutual agreement pacts with other nations for joint control. Thus, space law, like international law, will probably develop according to relative power of various nations, instead of through any master plan. The failure to perceive the power realities is the major flaw in the workability of the air-space theory.

2. *Jenks' Free Space Theory*

Dr. C. Wilfred Jenks, an associate of the Institution of International Law at Cambridge, England, has written an interesting treatise on his concepts entitled, *International Law and Activities in Space* (1956), in which he propounds a free-space theory. Briefly, in a six-step intimation group space program, he theorizes that:

a. Space beyond the atmosphere is a *res extra commercia*, incapable by its nature of appropriation on behalf of any particular sovereignty. State sovereignty is limited to activities within the atmosphere, which would be similar in control to that which can be "exercised in territorial waters or over a wider maritime frontier belt."

b. It is most desirable that jurisdiction over activities in space be tested in the United Nations.

c. Failing such a solution, jurisdiction will have to be determined by analogies to maritime and aviation law.

d. Rules will be necessary to protect national authorities in space.

e. The sovereignty of the Moon should be vested in the United Nations.

f. The natural resources of the Moon should be vested in the United Nations (and any exploitation should be on a lease from that organization).

Although the Jenks theory appears to be more realistic than that of Schachter from a cold power competition standpoint, it too has a flaw in that it establishes an illogical state sovereignty power control limit at the edge of the atmosphere. Will a nation that perfects a device which can penetrate and exercise a degree of control over outer space declare its sovereignty ends at the edge of the atmosphere, where space begins? Some moralistic nations might acquiesce to such a hypothetical limit, but not amoral ones, of which unfortunately there are a few left in the world.

3. Haley's International Unanimity Theory

Andrew G. Haley, a prominent present-day international space lawyer, who is general counsel for the American Rocket Society and president of the International Astronautical Federation, has written several articles (some of which were originally prepared as speeches) on the general subject of space law. In one of his more comprehensive tomes, he propounds a theory, which for want of a better title, we can call the International Unanimity Theory.

In the theory Haley goes beyond Jenks, as he envisions the possibility that areas above the atmosphere (roughly 300 miles and up) *might* be subject to sovereign control by one or more nations. But the now-historic fact, that *no* nations objected to the possibility of Earth satellite vehicles traversing their sovereign territories during the IGY, leads Haley to conclude that the sovereignty of space has been, *ipso facto*, turned over to the United Nations. This mutual understanding will undoubtedly continue as long as outer space is to be used for peaceful, exploratory purposes, or as long as no one nation has the ability to intercept a satellite or space missile. Haley also feels that the "scientists in the IGY program have benefited mankind as a whole in a field where the lawyers might well have failed."

He concludes that the present body of international law, based on maritime jurisdiction and restricted aviation law, is entirely "hostile" to the realities of space flight and is therefore inadequate. This inadequacy applies to both civil space-flight rules and rules of space war. This weakness is the reason why a new system of space law, based on the principle of fundamental justice through the United Nations, is needed.

More recently Haley, in a coast-to-coast space law debate after sputnik, stated that he felt ". . . under certain conditions, national jurisdiction will be quite indirectly but effectively maintained over contiguous space." This will be true when the nations of the Earth are offered point-to-point rocket communications, with the trajectories of these routes reaching different altitudes.

"National jurisdiction will be effectively maintained by the granting of launching and landing rights, and thus there will be indirect national control with respect to point-by-point earth rockets over contiguous space. . . ." He correctly points out that "the very problems of locating instrumentation along the manifold aerodynamic and non-aerodynamic routes, orbits and trajectories, will require the highest degree of cooperation and regulation for the operational efficiency and safety of all concerned."

Haley's step-by-step plan, which he feels must be taken to establish such a system of international space law, beginning with a mutual agreement on space communications, has merit. However, he does not think it likely that any nation, with the capability to reach out into space, would break a United Nations agreement. He offers no alternative plan if such an unfortunate event should occur, as he seems to have absolute faith in the peace-making machinery of the United Nations to solve any potential or actual space conflict problems around the conference table.

4. Cooper's Control Theory

John Cobb Cooper, the dean of American International Air Lawyers, formerly vice president of Pan American Airways and formerly a director of the Institute of International Air Law at McGill University, Montreal, Canada, has fathered a power theory of space control, which is unlimited in its scope. It is based on the assumption that a nation's ability to govern events occurring over its territory varies only with the nation's ability to penetrate up into space.

According to this theory, one nation may not be able to launch a vehicle which can escape the confines of the Earth's atmosphere, while another one may be able to reach out well beyond the space frontiers.

Realizing the efficacy of this potential future space rivalry, Cooper proposed that an amendment to the 1944 Chicago Convention be adopted to restrict the pure spacepower enthusiasts, whoever they might be. (*See* Fig. 18.)

He feels that full state sovereignty could be maintained in the territorial atmospheric space. He believes that in any new agreement we should reaffirm Article One of the Chicago Convention "giving the subjacent state full sovereignty in the areas of atmospheric space above it, up to the height where aircraft, as now defined, may be operated." However, he felt that state sovereignty should rule, subject to the right of transit for non-military flight instrumentalities when ascending or descending.

After the Soviets announced the successful launching of their ICBM's, Cooper revised his thinking on the upper limits for national sovereign control of air space in a letter to *The London Times* on September 2, 1957. "In view of the claims now made by [Major General] Pokrovsky that guided missiles will traverse upper space at least 600 miles above the surface of the earth, it is apparent to me that my own views must be revised. Obviously, no neutral state can permit the space above it to be used as an area for the passage of guided missiles designed to cause destruction in a distant state."

In space itself, he feels that this outer area should be kept free for the passage of *all* instrumentalities, be they military or civilian, with any nation having the right to launch space-flying vehicles as high and as far as it wishes.

This state of affairs was predicted by Gen. Bernard A. Schriever at the first United States Air Force Astronautical Symposium held in February, 1957, when he acquiesced readily to the idea of using forthcoming ICBM's as a lever for United States exploration of space. This prediction seemed to support Cooper's thesis.

However, according to Haley, Cooper's rule of space control presents the disquieting prospect that a state with extraordinary scientific resources could extend an empire into deep space. It is a counterpart of the might makes right principle which pervades maritime law and which kept England Mistress of the Seas for centuries. This rule imposes a limit over national sovereignty which gives Cooper's theory an empirical limit.

The trouble with Cooper's control theory is that it limits sovereignty only on the basis of relative state power. Nations that possess the capability to blast any satellite or missile from the skies, regardless of their purpose, could do so at will, at the same time other nations were helpless to do anything about various types of spacecraft passing over their territory or to intervene in support of a friendly space-exploring nation.

5. Heinrich's Universe in Motion Theory

The last noteworthy theory in "metalaw" (space law) has been proposed by Dr. Wolf Heinrich, grandson of Kaiser Wilhelm and presently Prince of Hanover and Duke of Brunswick, in his Ph.D. thesis, "Air Law and Space" (1953). Dr. Heinrich, who is credited with writing the first recorded doctoral dissertation in this embryonic field, says that the authorities agree that the Earth's atmosphere extends to a height of some 196 miles, where the last traces of gas are found that are considered to belong to the Earth's air envelope. Beyond this limit is "space," which includes all the other stars and planets.

Heinrich therefore believes that international sovereignty cannot extend beyond the Earth's atmosphere, because beyond that "everything in the universe is in motion; nothing is constant." He asserts that, as a practical matter, the exercise of national sovereignty in a region that does not stand still and cannot be defined "could never be effective."

He concludes that when mankind ceases to be earthbound, "conventional legal conceptions, whether of national or international law, will have to be abandoned," and that there must not be a "blind imposition of present law upon situations for which it was never made. . . . But where the sovereignty of the state ended, it must not be assumed that the moral obligations of men cease. On the contrary," he continues, "they follow them wherever they may go. All laws, whether regarded hitherto as national or international, concerned with morals, decency and fair and honorable conduct, whether on the part of state, of corporations or of private individuals must remain."

The trouble with the Prince of Hanover's thesis is that literally interpreted he would seem to be propounding an "anarchy" of space. His stressing of flexibility, due to the fact that the Universe is always in a state of flux and perpetual motion, would seem to rule out any set of fixed legal boundaries or rules. Such a reliance on purely moral persuasion to ensure that man will act properly in space seems to be a Utopian dream that shirks reality.

The Five Theories in Retrospect

The problem of ownership of the Universe and outer space, envisaged by the five theories previously examined, shows no universally agreed concept of space control or law. However, certain common assumptions seem to be held by all the theorists studied, regardless of their differences on application of individual theses of space law and rules.

One of these assumptions is the general agreement that there is an inherent conflict between the doctrine of freedom of the seas and that of state sovereignty over territorial air space, with the former rules seeming to apply more readily to vehicles flying in outer space, rather than the latter which pertains to state sovereignty control now outmoded. The inability of present rigid "air curtains" over fixed territorial boundaries to adapt themselves to the constant changes of spatial relationships of a space vehicle, due to the rotation of the Earth, is the logical determinant which negates the present state sovereignty air law. All of the five theories, including their fallacies, propose some limit on national air sovereignty, which should be enough proof to seal the coffin on this present doctrine and to prevent its application to space flight.

The next chapter presents a proposed Law of the Universe which will coincide with a new sixth theory of space law (See Chap. 13) aiming to overcome limitations of the foregoing five space law theories.

chapter 11

who owns the universe?

We will have to deal with different natures. The initial burden will be on the philosophers to come up with a new brand of natural law appropriate to the universe as we discover it. Perhaps centuries after that, we can look forward to the codification of a new pragmatic law administered, it may be, by a Court of Intergalactic Justice.

Andrew G. Haley
President, International Astronautical Federation

Now that we have examined some of the problems of establishing a workable law for space, we need to take a look at the legal problems relating to the discovery, ownership, and control of bodies in space—such as the Moon and the planets. This problem is even more complicated and may be harder to solve amicably than that of agreeing mutually to an international law for space itself.

If either the United States or Russia succeeds in landing a man on the Moon or even circumnavigating it, will this mean that the Moon has been discovered? Will this symbolic possession of a man setting foot on the Moon or setting up an unmanned radar beacon on our lunar satellite be enough evidence for claims to sovereignty?

Past international law would hint that these precedents would be sufficient to establish sovereignty, but fortunately international law is a living organism that has passed through many evolutionary stages in the past. So it appears that the principles

and precedents of international law of the past do not apply
to sovereign control of celestial bodies.

Theoretically, though, the first nation to reach the Moon
and to establish a manned Moon base can make a sovereign
claim to the whole subplanet. In the absence of a mutually respected international law, the first nation to "plant its flag" or
a military weapon on the Moon could assert ownership and deny
access to all others.

Any appeals that will be made by other nations will only be
recognized if the United Nations has enough teeth to enforce
decisions made after such appeals. One pessimistic note on this
matter has been the relative lack of success of present international law to settle the status of the Antarctic—the closest analogy
to control of the Moon here on Earth.

For example, in May, 1955, the British Government insti-
tuted proceedings in the International Court of Justice against
Argentina and Chile, accusing them of encroaching on British
territory in the Antarctic. Ten months later, the Court set aside
the British challenge, as neither of the South American republics cared to acknowledge the Court's jurisdiction.

In 1948, the United States proposed an eight-power confer-
ence to settle the problem of jurisdiction over the Antarctic. The
British claimed to be willing to consider the proposition, but
Chile and Argentina did not, so the proposal was dropped.

A new turn of events occurred regarding the control of the icy
continent down under. In early January, 1958, the United States
Government announced that it may decide soon to drop its long-
held policy that no nation can stake a valid claim to Antarctic
territory.

The previous policy had been laid down in 1924, but recent
technological advances, plus the Soviet drive for power, have
given new strategic and tactical significance to this frozen land.

Washington diplomats said on January 3, 1958, that there
were four possible alternatives to the present policy (all of which
are analogous to future control of the Moon):

1. The United States, which has six Antarctic bases, including

one at the South Pole, could claim all areas not previously claimed by others.

2. The United States could propose internationalizing Antarctica, possibly through the United Nations. (The British are pushing this proposal now).

3. The United States could join with other American republics in claiming all of Antarctica south of Cape Horn. This would be an extension of the Monroe Doctrine to the South Pole, and was suggested originally by President Franklin D. Roosevelt in 1940, when Nazi Germany was conducting naval warfare in the area.

4. The ANZUS Pact allies (Australia, New Zealand, and the United States) could put forward claims. With Sir Edmund Hillary's and Dr. Vivian Fuchs' first successful overland treks to the Pole in forty-six years completed in January and February, 1958, this alternative takes on added significance.

At present, there is a kind of truce among all the countries having bases there, including the Soviet Union, with all cooperating in new explorations and scientific experiments during the International Geophysical Year. But when the IGY comes to an end on December 31, 1958, no one expects those countries, including Russia, who have established permanent bases there to pull out.

Strangely enough, the United States, Great Britain, and Russia all claim to have discovered the Antarctic Continent, in the same year—1820. Britain made the first official claim to the territory, however, in 1908, and was followed soon thereafter by Norway, Australia, France, New Zealand, Chile, and Argentina.

After the French advanced their claim in 1924, the then Secretary of State Charles Evans Hughes proclaimed this United States policy: "The discovery of lands unknown to civilization, even when coupled with a formal taking of possession, does not support a valid claim of sovereignty, unless discovery is followed by an actual settlement of the discovered country."

It is fairly obvious that we are not going to turn our backs on lunar conquest, for we would be cutting ourselves off from a

great adventure and an international destiny. Therefore, by
making plans to land on the Moon, we "might" be taking a
chance on meeting some other lunar explorers from the Earth
on our satellite, but chances are that those explorers would be
unable to prevent our landing, nor would their home nation
provoke a global Earth war because of a possible "trespassing"
incident. This latter alternative is practically unthinkable in our
present world. Rather, it is hopeful that negotiations between
the powers *within* the framework of the United Nations will
iron out any petty, narrow, nationalistic views over lunar jurisdiction.

Five Theories of Lunar Control and Ownership

Let us examine five leading theories of lunar control put
forth in advance of the first manned lunar vehicles to arrive on
the Moon.

1. National Lunar Subdivision Concept

Some authorities have expressed the view that the United
Nations should subdivide the lighted surface of the Moon on
behalf of the major Earth nations which signify the desire and
ability to explore and colonize their "pie slice" parcels. This
theory presupposes that mapmakers and legal experts on Earth
will be able to determine in advance of lunar development
precisely where one nation's claim begins and ends on the crater-
studded surface of the Moon.

2. Lunar "First Come—First Served"

Some may raise the question as to whether the Moon should
be considered simply as *res nullius*, free for occupation, in the
same way as the undiscovered parts of the Antarctic Continent.
It is possible that some governments will take advantage of this
theory and stake out claims in outer space.

This theory is based on the "first come, first served" concept, which was the unwritten but thoroughly understood basis for the exploration and conquest of the New World in the 16th and 17th centuries. Whoever reached an uncharted land first and planted his country's flag on the territory where his ship was beached claimed all the surrounding territory for his nation. This theory still holds true for the last great unexplored continent, Antarctica, where the major nations of the world have set up national scientific outposts along the periphery of the icy continent.

Proponents of this theory feel that a repetition of this present situation in the Antarctic could take place on the Moon, with small crater bases dotting the surface at scattered points.

In the Antarctic today (the continent with the closest geopolitical similarities to the Moon), none of the claims of the various nations which have established bases there during the IGY or previously have as yet been recognized by competent international bodies. This includes the corridors surveyed by aircraft, as well as the land explored on foot or with the aid of dog sleds and Snocats. So the Antarctic and the Moon could be considered gigantic no man's lands—until recognition of sovereignty by a recognized world agency, such as the United Nations.

3. *National Lunar Corridor Concept*

As manned spaceships travel over various portions of the Moon's crust from close-in orbits, it is possible that the navigators of the spaceships will lay claim to wide corridor stretches of the Moon for their national homeland. If such a series of events should come to pass, disputes probably will arise over the ownership of space-mapped or tractor-explored lunar surfaces where the corridors overlap. The Antarctic corridor surveyed by Sir Edmund Hillary and Dr. Vivian Fuchs in their overland dashes to the South Pole in late 1957 and early 1958 could theoretically be claimed by both New Zealand and Britain.

4. An International UN Lunar Concept

By far the most feasible theory for control and exploration of the Moon is the one that envisions our natural Earth satellite under the complete jurisdiction of the United Nations. This theory presupposes that no fixed islands or corridors on the Moon would be leased or claimed by any one nation, but rather all of the lunar surface and its natural resources would be owned and controlled by the United Nations on behalf of all the peoples of the Earth, probably under the Trusteeship Council.

The co-operation among the many nations in the Antarctic during the current International Geophysical Year is an argument for internationalizing that continent. The extensive scientific research being carried on there by representatives from the twelve nations on a co-operative basis might set a pattern for future United Nations co-operation on control of the Moon and the planets, that will be of benefit to all mankind.

One outcome of a definitive future UN Space Law Code (in the absence of the knowledge of other life on the planets), as it applies to the Moon for instance, would be that the Earth and its peoples would mutually control and own the Moon and space. This thesis would contradict the current one heard many times recently, that he who controls the Moon controls the Earth.

5. The Dark Side Concept

A related question still to be explored is the future ownership of the dark side of the Moon. How will this half of our natural satellite be controlled and used? Only time and a resolving of decisions affecting ownership and control of the light side will help to solve this problem.

Our galaxy, which is called the Milky Way, contains roughly 400 billion stars. One expert astronomer, Dr. Gerard Kuiper, director of the Yerkes Observatory, believes that about 10 billion of the stars do have planets orbiting around them. If we assume that our own planetary Solar System is typical, then we can estimate that there are at least 100 *billion planets in our*

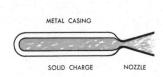

The Solid-Propellant Rocket Motor

The solid-propellant rocket motor is the simplest form of rocket propulsion. It has no moving parts and in its standard form is noted for its high operational reliability. Its development in the past few years has been phenomenal and has reached a point where it is being considered for ICBM applications.

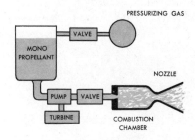

II. The Liquid Monopropellant Rocket Engine

A monopropellant rocket engine is the simplest form of liquid rocket engine. The monopropellant is a liquid containing both the fuel and the oxidizer required to support combustion. The monopropellant is fed to the thrust chamber by a pressurizing gas or by a turbine pump as illustrated. The more accepted feed technique of the two is the pressure feed.

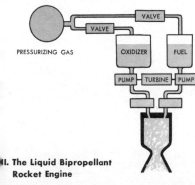

III. The Liquid Bipropellant Rocket Engine

Of all the types of rocket engines commonly used in today's missile, the liquid bipropellant is the most complex, yet the most widely used of the family of liquid rocket engines. It is the type found in our IRBM's and ICBM's. This type of system carries two liquids, one of which is the oxidizer and the other the fuel. Propellants are fed to the thrust chamber by a pressurizing gas or turbine pump—however, in this type of system the turbine pump feed is favored.

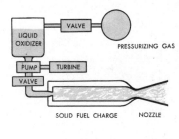

IV. The Liquid-Solid Propellant Rocket Engine

This type of rocket engine is generally referred to as a "hybrid" engine. It consists of a solid fuel charge (somewhat similar in shape to the solid motor) and a liquid oxidizer. This engine has been operated successfully, but has not been generally accepted for a specific application.

Fig. 9—Types of rocket engines—how they operate.

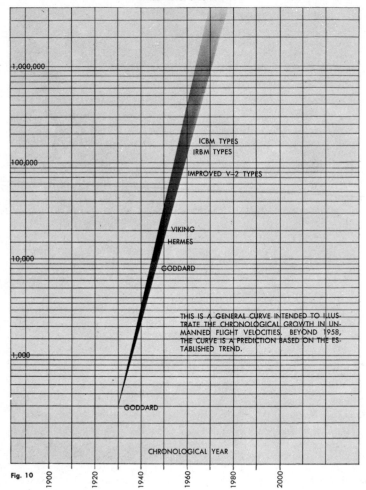

ONE-HUNDRED-YEAR PROGRESS

AMERICAN ROCKET ENGINES
THRUST-LEVEL SPECTRUM

ENGINE THRUST LEVEL—POUNDS

1,000,000

100,000

ICBM TYPES
IRBM TYPES
IMPROVED V–2 TYPES

VIKING
HERMES

10,000

GODDARD

THIS IS A GENERAL CURVE INTENDED TO ILLUS-
TRATE THE CHRONOLOGICAL GROWTH IN UN-
MANNED FLIGHT VELOCITIES. BEYOND 1958,
THE CURVE IS A PREDICTION BASED ON THE ES-
TABLISHED TREND.

1,000

GODDARD

CHRONOLOGICAL YEAR

Fig. 10

1900   1920   1940   1960   1980   2000

galaxy alone. With over 100 billion galaxies in the Universe, the number of planets, with or without life, is multiplied to an astronomical figure.

If these other galaxies are like ours, then at least 10 percent or 10 billion planets in each galaxy, including ours, are orbiting in a temperate life zone, at just the proper distance from their sun so that water, air, and vital elements would exist. With these basic chemical properties in abundance, then life of some sort probably does exist on those planets.

Based on the mathematical theory of probability, it is therefore inconceivable that ours is the "only" inhabitable planet out of the 10 billion in our galaxy, where conditions are right for the evolution of life. It is possible that on other planets life has been evolving for millions of years longer than it has been doing on Earth. This fact is worth pondering, as we plan in the future to build spaceships to other star systems.

As was said in Chapter 1, "Why Go into Space?", let us hope that man will be such a matured moral person when he is traveling to a distant planet in another star system that he will exercise proper application of his ethical principles, if and when he confronts creatures from other galaxies. Man's thoughts and deeds will then be put to their greatest test.

What other steps shall man take beyond thoughts of control of the Moon to extend his visions to control of the Universe? As an interesting legal exercise and conversation piece, it is worth pondering a moment what these future legal principles might be like.

Four Laws for Control of the Universe

The broad outlines of four legal principles for future control of the Universe are propounded for consideration:

1. Control of Unoccupied Bodies by the Earth

With the control of the Moon being a symbol and a precedent for the control of all unoccupied bodies in our Universe, the foregoing lunar control concepts will become a test case in applications for future peaceful explorations and exploitations of other similar bodies.

Where the Moon is a celestial body without inhabitants and with no known prior claims by any other inhabited outer-space body, the problems of control of celestial bodies where life exists will be more complicated.

2. Control of Unoccupied Bodies Between the Earth and Extragalactic Bodies

Most experts feel that there is little chance of life as we know it in our planetary system, so the legal aspects of prior claims to "dead" moons and planets in our planetary or another planetary system by representatives from other star systems or galaxies is worth consideration.

We do not want to become embroiled in any interstellar or intergalactic conflict over real-estate control over unoccupied bodies, which may be of little practical significance to us in extending ourselves into the Universe. The question of our legal rights and our actions, if such a situation should arise, is a moral one as well as a political one.

3. Control of Celestial Bodies Which Possess Life

The chances are that the first space explorers from the Earth will discover life on one of the bodies in the Universe. If they do, the problem will not be a fight for control of the body in question between the Earth and some other galactic planet, but between the Earth and the creatures of the celestial body itself. In this category, it is the responsibility of our representatives who first set foot on the surface of some far-flung planet possessing life to respect the rights of others.

This principle should apply to the moons and asteroids of the larger life-possessing planets, if they, too, feature some sort of rational life that is capable of communicating with our Earthmen.

It is believed that Titan, one of Saturn's moons, is the only moon in our planetary system that has an atmosphere and which may possess life. In the near future, this body could be one of the most hotly contested spheres between the Earth and some other celestial body.

In any instance where there is reason to believe that intelligent life exists on a planet, Andrew Haley says that "no earth space ship may land without having satisfactorily ascertained that the landing and contact will injure neither the explorer nor the explored, and until the earth ship has been invited to land by the explored."

The Golden Rule has no application in this type of situation, according to Haley, because "to treat others as we would desire to be treated might well mean their destruction."

4. Control of Occupied Bodies with Prior Claims from other Galaxies

This last principle will probably be the most complicated of all to settle, should Earth representatives of the future try to claim some "rich" occupied planet which is already under the suzerainty of some other galactic planet. In such a case, we will really need a workable Court of Intergalactic Justice to iron out the differences.

We have had some good experience here on Earth with a similar situation on a smaller scale. We are referring, of course, to the long-standing dispute over Kashmir, an occupied territory, which is being claimed by both India and Pakistan. For the past six years, the United Nations, mainly through its representative, Frank Graham of the United States, has been acting as a *de facto* Court of Worldly Justice to settle the dispute amicably. That this dispute has not flared into a broader one with more serious bloodshed is a tribute to the United Nations efforts. Such examples, when multiplied in the future, will serve as training grounds for setting up a permanent Court of Intergalactic Justice.

The Challenge of the Universe

The challenge of the Universe to man, who will be transported by propulsion systems that will come through advances in the state-of-the-art in astronautics, is the supreme challenge today. Future generations will have to find adequate solutions to the problems of living in other parts of the Universe, which gives our life on Earth its ultimate meaning.

In this respect, the authors do not agree with the conclusions of a recognized authority on space travel, who recently wrote that we should not, however, let ourselves be stampeded into frantic attempts to "prove" a need for rushing to Venus or Mars, because, to put it bluntly, there really is none *today*. This type of philosophical thinking about present-day planning for future penetrations by man into the Universe can only stunt our growth and dwarf our thinking. As a nation, thinking of this type has hurt the United States in the past. On the contrary, as we have already pointed out, there are many excellent reasons for going into the Universe—*now*.

Man should set his sights on dispersing himself and his descendants through the Universe and thus fulfill his destiny. This goal, to be reached by co-operating with the laws of nature and his own moral principles, will rid man of the limitations that he has imposed upon himself. In the infinite extreme, it is only man himself that can shackle his body and his thoughts to this Earth.

It is up to man to extend his vision into the Universe, so that he may start planning today for a tomorrow that will make his life really worth living.

chapter 12

the first steps to control space

Of course, anything [a Soviet attack on the U. S.] is possible in this world in which we live . . . but I say this: the
likelihood that any nation possessing these great weapons
of massive destruction would use them in an attack, grows
less, I think, every year. I believe that as their understanding of them grows, then the less the chance that they
would go on an adventure that brought these things into
play, because as I see it, any such *operation today is just
another way of committing suicide*. (Authors' italics.)

President Dwight D. Eisenhower
Press Conference—February, 1957

PRESIDENT EISENHOWER devoted one sentence in his
State of the Union message to Congress on January 10, 1957,
to the problem of international control of the most fantastic
weapons of modern warfare that mankind has ever wrought.
In the course of his speech, he stated that "We are willing to
enter any reliable agreement which would . . . mutually control the outer space missile and the earth satellite development."
Four days later, the Chief Delegate to the United Nations from
the United States, Henry Cabot Lodge, reiterated this request as
part of the American Five Point Program on Disarmament.

Mr. Lodge told the United Nations that international inspection of programs for using Earth satellites, intercontinental missiles, and other objects in outer space was a "first step" toward
reserving the upper limits of the Earth "exclusively" for science
and peace.

Chronology of the First International Steps for Long-Range Missile Control

A missile-control proposal, if agreed upon by representatives of the Soviet Union and of the United States would be a step closer to President Eisenhower's dream of mutual aerial inspection. This proposal was met with a Soviet counterproposal on November 17, 1957, when Russia called for a summit conference on disarmament and tentatively agreed to aerial inspection survey flights within a 500-mile corridor over the borders of participating countries. This Soviet proposal was the first positive gesture toward the ultimate goal of mutual control of the long-range missiles, and came several years after the President's first challenging plan (1955) for mutual aerial inspection.

On April 25, 1957, during the course of the United Nations disarmament talks in London, the United States urged disarmament steps to bar the use of outer space for weapons ranging from intercontinental missiles to space platforms for war. American delegate, Harold Stassen, told the five nation subcommittee that the United States is ready to consider proposals that would prevent development of the outer-space nuclear weapon missile— a complete ban.

With none of these weapons yet in actual operation, he said, the United States believed that an agreement not to build them would be a significant advance, reserving outer space for peaceful purposes. It would be far easier to work out a control system for the weapons now than after they are in operation, he told the subcommittee.

On the same day, however, the Soviet representative, Valerian A. Zorin, Deputy Foreign Minister of the Soviet Union, countered that his country wants to go far beyond that. He said Russia wants a ban on missiles that travel through all space, including even short-range missiles that carry nuclear warheads.

Zorin's counterproposal represented the general Russian position on barring nuclear weapons in all forms. Russia has been increasingly sensitive about rockets, since recently, the United States plans to provide its forces in countries of the North Atlantic Treaty Organization (NATO) with tactical atomic weapons and to give Great Britain and other NATO countries intermediate range missiles.

The feeling at the time, however, among the participants was that the showdown phase of the talks would come later. The five nations represented were the United States, Russia, Great Britain, France, and Canada. They did not grapple with this major problem again until July 25, when the United States proposed that an international committee be established to fix the terms of a ban on the military use of intercontinental missiles.

The proposal was again made by Mr. Stassen before the same United Nations Disarmament Subcommittee still meeting in London. He said a board of technical experts on missiles should be set up as part of a first-step arms-reduction pact three months after the agreement had become effective. Its task would be to formulate a system that would ensure the use of outer-space missiles for peaceful purposes only.

Mr. Stassen warned the group that an "uncontrolled race through the outer space in years to come would lead to a great tragedy for mankind." He also warned of the dangers of long-range missiles armed with nuclear warheads. His July 25 proposal was a refinement of the one made exactly three months before, but with the addition of the committee of experts as a practical first step toward the earlier goal.

The United States wants to restrict the use of long-range missiles to purely scientific purposes. In explaining the proposal, United States representatives mentioned the experiments in gathering data from outer space that are being conducted in connection with the International Geophysical Year. The Vanguard Earth satellite launching program, the Air Force's Project Far Side, and the Aerobee-Hi research rockets are but a few of the more publicized examples of what these representatives were referring to. It is significant to note that these rockets were conceived originally as purely scientific devices; whereas the ICBM's, which are military weapons, might revert to predominantly scientific vehicles by conversions and modifications in their testing components.

The British, French, and Canadian delegates supported the new United States proposals; the Soviet delegation said it would study them. Valerian A. Zorin linked the problem of missiles to the Soviet proposals for a complete ban on the use of all nuclear weapons.

Mr. Stassen emphasized that in the opinion of the United States all missiles and rockets fell within the terms of a first-step disarmament pact. He said that these should be included among the arms to be set aside under systems of control and inspection.

The committee to deal with the problems of ICBM's, according to United States sources, should be made up of representatives of all signatories to a first-step arms reduction accord. The committee suggested that such representatives should be scientists who could decide the importance of such projectiles in peaceful research.

The same sources, according to *The New York Times*, indicated that the proposal for the control of long-range missiles would become clearer after the United States plan for inspection zones had been presented. This plan followed the recommendations on missiles and rockets and was presented by Secretary of State John Foster Dulles on August 2. It envisioned a three-part Western proposal of aerial- and ground-inspection zones, with the first zone covering all of the United States, Alaska, Canada, and the Soviet Union. If the Soviets failed to accept this sweeping inspection zone plan, then a second smaller zone, covering only the northern approaches to the United States and Russia, plus a third European zone, would be debated. At this time, the Soviets have gone on record as denouncing this plan, particularly the comprehensive first-step inspection zone, for a variety of reasons.

One element of the earlier (July 25) missile-control plan was a suggestion to have international regulation and inspection of launching bases according to United States informants at the London talks. Although Mr. Stassen believes that the barring of the development of ICBM's for military purposes is "an inescapable proposal for the first step" in world arms limitations, another United States spokesman emphasized that there would have to be an accepted inspection system before any ban on ICBM's could be imposed.

The next event occurred when one of the items buried in the Western package proposal made before the London Disarmament Conference on August 29, 1957, expressed the hope that a means could be found to use future intercontinental ballistic missiles for scientific purposes only.

Although this portion of the proposal was dwarfed by the greater emphasis on limitation and control of nuclear weapons and aerial inspection, it does signify a significant step forward in the thinking of many Western diplomats, who are sincerely attempting to find a solution to the problem of global disarmament. A spark of an idea on peaceful uses of ICBM's for contiguous space flight was put on the diplomats' table at last.

The Russians rejected all of the Western disarmament proposals, including the suggestion to seek ways to adapt ICBM's for scientific purposes proposed on the following day, with a tough denunciation speech by Valerian A. Zorin. Russia had announced to the world her winning of the race to the 5,000-mile-long-range missile in the last week of August, just prior to the Western disarmament proposal, so she was in a position to exert her new power strength to the utmost.

The Soviets assumed a propaganda role to impress the rest of the world with their new military spacepower dimension and their confidence and faith in it. For the first time they had beaten the West in a major technological race, by perfecting the long-range missile first, after having come in second at the A-bomb and H-bomb tape. Even though they were somewhat vague in their announcement of August 27, 1957, of the successful testing of their ICBM as to its target accuracy, etc., the fact stood out that many respected observers in the West, including such diverse elements as the U. S. State Department, *The New York Times*, and Gen. Lauris Norstad, Supreme Commander of NATO, all believed that the Russians were not bluffing. *Komsomol Pravda*, the Communist youth paper, called the ICBM missile "the crowning point" in Soviet weapons development. The launching of the sputniks in October and November of 1957 confirmed this statement and ended all doubts about the Soviets having an ICBM.

Whether Russia will attain sufficient quantities of these ultimate weapons in operational readiness is the next immediate goal of the second lap of the ICBM race—the Soviets having won the initial test heat. It has been confirmed that the Soviets had achieved a successful assembly line production of modified and probably improved German V-2's, thus setting the stage for mass production of any type of missile. Senator Henry Jackson from the State of Washington, who is an expert on such matters, feels that Russia will be able to produce great quantities of ICBM's now that she has successfully tested prototypes. With a sufficient quantity on hand, Russia need have no fear of allocating a significant amount for scientific tests. According to the dominant opinion at the London talks at the time of the Russian rejection of the U. S. disarmament proposals, world feeling was and is strongly in favor of obtaining some kind of disarmament agreement, so there is a chance that the Soviet boasts and show of strength may backfire.

Such a "backfire" would be in the minds of men, caused by the underlying moral issues involved. The issue, of whether the potential military or peaceful uses of ICBM's will predominate, is the supreme problem of our time. The London talks had hinted at a plan for scientific uses of long-range missiles several months prior to Russia's shocking announcement about the first sputnik. The Soviets had successfully tested at least four of their ICBM's by the end of August, according to General Norstad, while the first two tests of a prototype Atlas ICBM in the United States in the latter part of 1957 fizzled after component failures led to their destruction at 10,000 feet. And the third Atlas fired in December, 1957, was only a limited success.

Unfortunately, as far as the cause of international control was concerned, one of the first bombastic acts of the Soviets after their successful sputnik launching was to withdraw from the United Nations disarmament deliberations, which had apparently been making some worthwhile headway prior to that earth-shaking event.

On September 19, 1957, Secretary of State Dulles, in pleading before the UN General Assembly for the adoption of Western proposals, which the Soviets called a "sham," said: "The joint proposals would, among other things, . . . establish a study of outer space to the end that it shall be used only for peaceful, not military purposes. The Soviet Union has announced that it has discovered ways to use outer space to wreak vast destruction anywhere. That is no new discovery," he added. "The United States knows how that can be done. Our task is to see that it is not done."

Eleven days later, and just four days prior to the launching of sputnik I, Henry Cabot Lodge told the Disarmament Commission: "We seek agreement on measures to control the newest threat to peace: The outer space missile. The weapon is too new for us to be able to present precise and detailed proposals to deal with it. But it is potentially so dangerous that it cannot be ignored. We propose . . . that means be designed to assure that the sending of objects through outer space will be for exclusively scientific and peaceful purposes."

Two weeks later, the United States, with British and other Western allied support, wanting to start general talks on the control of space missiles and Earth satellites without waiting for an overall disarmament agreement, found themselves stymied when the Soviets walked out of the Disarmament Commission. The Russians played their new psychological and military advantage to the hilt. Prior to October 4, 1957, they had seemingly been negotiating on disarmament in earnest for five months, but their post-sputnik diplomacy walkout made grim sense. Moscow felt by that time that she had the whip hand and did not need to make concessions.

On October 5, 1957, James T. Mangan, who claims he founded the Nation of Celestial Space, protested the Russian satellite launching as "an unprovoked trespassing into my territory." Mangan, a sixty-year-old public relations consultant from Chicago, said he was going to notify the Russians by letter of their violation of his territory.

He claimed that he homesteaded outer space December 21,

1948, by declaring its existence and writing a charter. The charter was filed January 18, 1949, in the Cook County Recorder's office, after a favorable legal opinion from the Illinois State's attorney.

Mangan named his frontier nation "Celestia," and said the trade-mark was approved by the U. S. Patent Office a week before the first sputnik was launched. His new nation's Grand Seal had been approved a year previously.

When he was asked whether he was going to shoot down the manmade moon, Mangan retorted, "The Nation of Celestial Space works more on the principle of moral persuasion than force." So far his moral persuasion has not prevented the sputniks from being launched since his protest.

Mr. Mangan's protest seemed to be the only one that had been made in the immediate period following the launching of the first sputnik. As no major or minor nation complained of the sputnik's flying over its sovereign territory, one conclusion was reached: that for all practical purposes, *space belonged to no one nation or person.*

On October 11, one week after the first sputnik satellite had been launched, twenty-one nations, including Canada, France, Great Britain, and the United States, introduced into the UN General Assembly a draft disarmament resolution which urged disarmament agreement to include the study "of an inspection system designed to ensure that the sending of objects through outer space will be exclusively for peaceful and scientific purposes." No definition of outer space seems to have come out of those deliberations.

The introduction of this important resolution strongly supports the argument that national sovereignty, in the eyes of the sponsors, does not exist in outer space. If it did, these nations would not be propounding multilateral inspection agreements pertaining to the type of space-flight instrumentalities which would be permitted in outer space.

Four Reasons for the International Control of Space Missiles

A brief analysis of the (1) *political*, (2) *economic*, (3) *military*, and (4) *psychosocial* significance of the space control statement by President Eisenhower in his 1957 message to Congress will help to provide a more comprehensive understanding of the deeper meaning and worth of his challenge to the world. Only after examining the significance of his statement from the four aspects already mentioned can one reach a balanced view of the possibilities of eventual international control of the ICBM. Ignoring any one of the four areas would present a distorted picture of the proper applications and controls of the intercontinental ballistic missiles of the future, which will travel at over 15,000 miles per hour.

Potentially, a foolproof mutual international setup for the control of long-range missiles and the satellites, which have both military and peaceful uses, will do more toward ensuring the survival of civilization as we know it than any single act.

1. The Political Significance of the International Control of the Outer-Space Missiles

One of the first conclusions drawn from the President's announcement was the fact that, for the first time in modern history, a head of a great nation had called for controls over a family of weapons *before* they had been put into operational use. This preoperational control approach is just the reverse of previous attempts to curb weapons of war, which heretofore had come only *after* the weapons had been used to kill combatants and civilians, or had at least been tested fully in prototype form. This procedure of post testing and postoperational international control attempts has held true for the A- and H-bombs, as it has done traditionally for the conventional weapons of war, such as tanks, submarines, and airplanes.

After years of false attempts to control and disarm the world's arsenal of weapons, we can discern a crack which has opened in the door toward eventual complete agreement between the

major nations on this vital matter of survival. Such an agreement, if carried to its ultimate fruition, might very well lead to
the establishment of a UN Air and Space Force, modeled along
the lines of the present embryonic UN Police Force guarding
the Suez region of Egypt. This first truly international police
force is now a historic fact and is setting a precedent and the
necessary groundwork for the establishment of a UN Air and
Space Force. This Space Force would possess United Nations
controlled missiles, satellites, and nuclear weapons, transferred
by the major powers to the United Nations arsenal.

Unlike a manned weapon, either on the land, sea, or in the
air, the unmanned outer-space missiles and Earth satellites pose
some delicate international, political, and diplomatic problems.
A prelude of things to come, which was embarrassing to those
on the inside, and which provided chuckles to many on the outside, concerned the first subsonic intercontinental guided missile, the Snark, which went astray sometime during the first
week in December, 1956. This missile ended up somewhere in
the jungles of Brazil, after being lost by its trackers and control
personnel at Cape Canaveral, Florida.

Suppose the Snark test vehicle, or some similar missile, had
landed in the middle of a teeming metropolis in Europe or
South America, instead of in the uninhabited Amazonian equa-
torial jungle? The diplomatic and political repercussions against
the United States would have been far more severe than that
which Japan heaped upon it after her fishing boat, *The Lucky
Dragon*, was caught in an H-bomb test's radioactive fall-out with
the eventual loss of one seaman's life. Under an internationally
controlled missile program, a United Nations agency would ab-
sorb the responsibility for any "stray" test missiles, rather than
the criticism being heaped on a single nation.

Short of accomplishing a ban on long-range missile tests as a
step toward total disarmament, a more practical intermediate
step toward sharing the costs and know-how of guided missiles
was taken in February, 1957, by a joint agreement between the
new British Defense Minister, Duncan Sandys, and the then
U. S. Secretary of Defense, Charles Wilson. The agreement

reached at the conclusion of the Sandys' mission to pool U. S. research and development on ballistic missiles controlled fusion with Great Britain as well as the leasing of actual United States missiles to England, without their atomic warheads, were the first steps toward international co-operation which could ultimately lead to international control of these weapons.

2. Economic Significance of Long-Range Missile Control

The tremendous cost of the present missile program in terms of natural resources and manpower has forced the United States into a top-level national control over production and future employment of long-range missiles. The Deputy Assistant Secretary of Defense for Research and Development, William Holaday, was given additional responsibilities in October, 1957, by the Defense Secretary and the President to oversee the entire Army, Navy, and Air Force missile program. A new space manager, Roy Johnson, was also appointed to supervise all antimissile missiles and space programs. This is the first time in the nation's history that so many complications have arisen over the question of control of a single weapon of war. Previously, there had always been enough small arms, shells, and bombs to be shared by *all* the branches of the armed services.

Duplication of missile production efforts on an international level can be just as costly, in the long run, as on a national level. The costs of the competing Soviet missile programs must be more of a strain on Russia's economy than it is on that of the United States, and it could cause a probable greater cutback in her consumer goods production in order for her to be able to keep up with and possibly surpass the American missile program.

The monetary impact of the missile program in the United States can be examined if one dissects its largest peacetime budget in history, that which President Eisenhower sent to Congress on January 16, 1958. In his 1958 fiscal budget, composed of over 1,200 pages, the focus on missiles becomes sharper when one discovers that a large part of the two-billion-dollar increase over the 1957 budget will go for more research and development in the guided-missile field. The total missile outlay for fiscal 1958 will come to over $2,540,000,000, or 8 percent of the Air Force weapons production. The outlay for missiles (for fiscal 1959) will be even larger—by at least $2,000,000,000 more—which resulted mainly as an aftermath of sputnik. This is more than the United States spent during the four years of World War II on the then-secret atomic bomb project which seemed so extravagant and such a big gamble at the time.

3. *The Military Significance of International Control of the Outer-Space Missile*

The extreme range, speed, and destructive power of these superweapons, as compared to the present conventional manned bombers, demand a highly centralized command control system, both nationally, and ultimately internationally. The plans underway for international tracking and monitoring of the IGY Earth satellites, which cannot be adequately controlled and monitored by one single nation, is a case in point.

Colonel Richard S. Leghorn, a retired U. S. Air Force officer, pointed out before the Senate Disarmament subcommittee on March 7, 1956, that such a missile test ban, monitored by a network of international radar picket posts set up at agreed points in national territories, requires more relinquishment of national sovereignty in the traditional sense than does a nuclear test ban which can be monitored from the outside.

In commenting on this testimony and on the Soviet and American attitudes toward aerial inspection, Senator Hubert Humphrey, the chairman of the subcommittee, stated during the hearings held in Minneapolis on June 16, 1956, that "the physicists and the engineers and the scientists who have testified before us have told us that unless aerial inspection can be agreed to *before* the guided missile or the intercontinental missile has been perfected, and the launching platforms and the cities could be conveniently camouflaged or put underground, it may not be very meaningful even if you do get it. There have been those who have testified . . . that aerial inspection would be primarily helpful in that period of time when there was a movement of materials for launching sites and platforms, etc. Once they were underground, covered over and camouflaged, it would be very difficult to ascertain if they were there."

As a step toward international military control under an agency such as a UN Air Police Force, centralized control on a national level would be a justifiable first step. The theory of a single combined service control is simple to envision on paper, but might be difficult to achieve in practice due to interservice differences. These differences over the employment and control of the long-range missiles have already assumed greater magnitudes than did the eruption between the services almost a decade ago over the merits of manned B-36 bombers *vs.* aircraft carriers. Some such true unification step will undoubtedly have to be made in the near future as a preliminary step toward international control.

4. *The Psychosocial Significance of International Control of Outer-Space Missiles*

The calculated risk which the President of the United States took in offering his challenge to Congress, the United Nations, and the world, leaves a positive impact in the psychosocial area. If we look upon the President's offer to disarm and control the missile as just a propaganda weapon, we may find ourselves in the dilemma which Senator John O. Pastore of Rhode Island found himself before a Senate committee on January 16, 1957, when he told his fellow lawmakers: "If the Russians accept our January 14 plan for disarmament, we would have to start pulling away from it."

This ultimate weapon control dilemma, which we face, is dualistic in its scope, according to no less an authority than Thomas K. Finletter, ex-Secretary of the Air Force, who stated before the same Senate committee already mentioned, that "first we must seek the causes of conflicts and simultaneously we must attack the problem of disarmament." He went on to say that we cannot continue to produce more B-52's and ICBM's while the Soviets do the same with their Bisons, Badgers, and missiles, without eventually working for 100 percent mutual disarmament. The ex-Air Force Secretary concluded with this stark question, "Would the American people accept this fact?"

No one has seen fit to predict an answer to this question, for it will take much painstaking education of the American public and careful planning on the part of the political leaders before a positive answer can be given.

The late Senator Brien McMahon of Connecticut made a statement regarding the psychosocial import of the control of the atom just before his untimely death, which could also apply to the ICBM situation. He said: "It is our solemn obligation, I think, to lift our eyes above the lesser problems that seem to monopolize our time and to discuss and act upon what, by any standard, is the supreme problem before our country and the world." Now that the atomic and hydrogen warheads can be carried to their targets at 15,000 miles per hour, McMahon's prophetic words become more indelible, if we are to survive. Unfortunately, it is too early to foresee very clearly the long-range psychosocial impact of international control of the ICBM's.

President Eisenhower's aim in proposing the need for a plan to control space could be interpreted as a move to head off the destructive use of these untested weapons and to guarantee their use for predominantly peaceful purposes. This timing was probably based on the lesson of the atom, about which control attempts were proposed after its wartime use. There is a chance that the President's one-sentence proposal encouraging the formulation of plans to control outer-space vehicles may go down in history as being of more significance to the future of man on this planet than was former President Harry S. Truman's Point Four statement that grew into aid for the underdeveloped nations of the world, or Gen. George C. Marshall's "few words at Harvard," which later evolved into the well-known Marshall Plan for the reconstruction of Europe.

A few days after his State of the Union message, President Eisenhower reaffirmed his belief in the involvement of the

United States in the destiny of men everywhere in his second inaugural address. He sealed the coffin of isolationism forever with a funeral oration which stressed the following: "One truth must rule all we think and all we do. No people can live to itself alone. The unity of all who dwell in freedom is their only sure defense." The President continued: "The economic need of all nations—in mutual dependence—makes isolation an impossibility. Not even America's prosperity could long survive if other nations did not also prosper."

Then in apparent concession to the revolution that missiles are having on our established concepts of military security, he continued, "No nation can longer be a fortress, lone and strong and safe. And any people seeking such shelter for themselves, now can build only their own prison."

Those words must have taken on added significance for the President and the millions of onlookers at the subsequent inaugural parade, as Snark, Redstone, and Corporal missiles were presented for the first time to the public. The pushbutton missile weapons of the Atomic Age, as they passed the reviewing stand on their wheeled carriers and floats, were saluting a president, who, probably more than any other man on Earth, realized their potential destructiveness and the necessity to do something constructive about preventing them from ever being launched in an all-out war.

If the international control of outer-space missile and Earth satellite becomes a reality, then we can face the prospects of what will happen after the International Geophysical Year and the launchings of the first peaceful Earth satellites as an omen of world security for years to come. Man's moral conscience would be freed so that he could look up to the heavens and know that he no longer need have any fear that some shooting star he might see on a dark night could actually be the glow of a deadly warhead plunging down to annihilate him and his family.

Some Sage Advice for the Next Steps in Solving This Problem

In searching for guidelines for evolving an attitude that will make for an eventual graceful acceptance of the international control of all outer-space missiles by a concert of all nations, one can find no better philosophical framework than the words of a man who was vitally interested in the problems of the Universe. The timely words of Albert Einstein, coined a few years before his death, were aimed at the problem of the ultimate weapon, and can be applied just as cogently to the missile carriers of the H-bomb weapon *before* they are completely perfected, as they do to the H-bomb itself.

"Science," said the discoverer of relativity, "has brought forth this danger, but the real problem is in the minds and hearts of men. We will not change the hearts of other men by mechanisms but by changing our hearts and speaking bravely . . . when we are clear in heart and mind—only then shall we find courage to surmount the fear which haunts the world."

chapter 13

the need for a United Nations space law

Sober, responsible men with solid records of achievement are already looking beyond the missile to the issue of controlling outer space itself.

And they expect to see steps taken in that direction in their lifetime.

But it is obvious that control the exploration of outer space must be lodged in an agency where it will be given very serious attention.

There are conflicting views as to where this agency should be and how much authority it should have.

It will take time to resolve these views but a decision cannot be withheld indefinitely.

Senator Lyndon Johnson
Chairman of the U. S. Senate Preparedness
subcommittee—December 16, 1957

DURING the open hearings before the Senate Preparedness subcommittee in the waning days of 1957, not one of the Government officials, science experts, or chiefs of the military services who testified mentioned the possibility of the United Nations becoming the administrative body over a new Space Agency.

Many of them recognized the need for some sort of centralized institution to supervise a comprehensive space program, with most of them suggesting that its new home be either the Pentagon or the White House. These recommendations appeared to be mainly conceived within a parochial nationalistic frame of reference, with an apparent ignoring of the international legal conflicts which such an agency might engender.

If such an agency comes to pass, it appears it must and will have to work hand in glove with the United Nations in its long-range space planning no matter where it is located within the organizational framework of either the Federal Government or the United Nations. This is necessary because of the jurisdictional and legal problems that are bound to arise with the advent of space flight around the Earth and to the Moon, planets, and stars.

Dr. John P. Hagen, Director of Project Vanguard, commented on this problem in a statement to the press on January 4, 1958, when he called for the creation of a special civilian-headed agency to handle space projects within the Department of Defense. But he conceded that "in the future, the objectives might be of such a nature that they would transcend the Department of Defense. At such time, it might well be that a separate agency should be discussed." This realization of the broader scope of future space programs necessitates strong consideration of the United Nations as the logical institution to head such an undertaking because of the "objectives" and "legal points" involved.

The time has come also for the establishment of international space laws to ensure the security of the world. Some of the questions that such laws should attempt to answer are: May space vehicles legally hover over any country? Under what international law could a space satellite legally be shot down when it is discovered taking pictures of a sovereign nation's defense areas? Should a United Nations space law be implemented through the International Civil Aviation Organization or through some other United Nations agency still unborn?

Suppose one of the Soviet or American satellites is transformed into flaming metal fragments when it re-enters the Earth's atmosphere during its decay period. By chance, it might cause property damage or loss of life. Professor Quincy Wright, former president of the American Society of International Law, raised

the question of legal responsibility should a United States satellite land in the middle of Westminster Abbey.

Can the nation that launched satellites be held responsible,
even though they have left man's control after their launching?

A United Nations sponsored Space Code Convention will
probably have to be called soon, as the result of a joint resolution by the majority of the General Assembly, to modify and
extend the United Nations Charter to include jurisdiction in
outer space. Simultaneously with the calling of such a convention, the Secretariat could commence to make plans for the
establishment of a permanent UN Space Force to enforce such
a code.

The Future Fathers of a UN Space Code

There have been many suggestions as to who is best fitted to
serve on a panel to devise a Space Law Code which will be
practicable and worthy of adoption by the United Nations. The
International Astronautical Federation, in the fall of 1957, appointed a committee, consisting of four physicists and three
lawyers from the United States and Russia to define air space
and air-space jurisdiction.

Although the physicists may be able to set the scientific boundaries of inner and outer space, they alone are not in a position
to answer for all the other professional disciplines that are directly involved in space flight and who *should have a say in the
final Space Law Code*. Precedent was established in the famous
Supreme Court decision, May 17, 1954, when the nine Justices,
in the unanimous and historic decision on the public schools,
based their findings on the research of sociologists, educators,
and political scientists, rather than on *past law* alone.

Such precedents usually help to produce a better product that
is more acceptable to mankind where the legal base for solving
disputes and establishing patterns is broadened to include many
disciplines and experts. Experts in such fields as aerodynamics,
rocket propulsion, astronomy, space medicine, missile guidance,
diplomacy, philosophy, sociology, and mathematics, as well as

lawyers and physicists, will *all* have a hand in writing man's first comprehensive Space Law Code.

Such a UN Space Code Convention would probably be held in opposition to the feelings of Oscar Schachter, Director of the General Legal Division of the United Nations, who, among others, feels that the Law of the Universe should grow in the same manner as common law, from custom and practice. An attempt to codify it now, he thinks, might lead to suspicion and do more harm than good.

Significant Problems of a UN Space Code Convention

The first UN Space Code Convention will have many problems to solve. Besides grappling with the basic questions of ownership and height, it will have to define mutually and obtain agreement on the meaning of such terms as: "atmosphere," "space flight," "space vehicles," "air space."

Definition of Space

The United States, in assuming its present prominent role in the IGY, has served general notice that all space above 300 miles is free space, as neither this country nor Russia has attempted to secure the rights of passage from other nations. But neither have the two nations yet agreed to fix any hypothetical altitude or distance out as the beginning of outer space. It would appear that the United States would therefore not attempt to press for a line beyond 300 miles as the critical space border area, although it is conceivable that it might bargain for an altitude less than that. Some experts have felt that an invisible line at 50 miles above the Earth's surface, the upper limits of aerodynamic lift, should be the dividing line between air space and space.

Oscar Schachter states that "Any attempt to extend national sovereignty higher than the airspace is bound to involve difficulties. . . . Why not, then fix the limits at the upper boundary of airspace and no higher? Beyond the airspace, we would apply a system similar to that followed on the high seas. . . . A legal

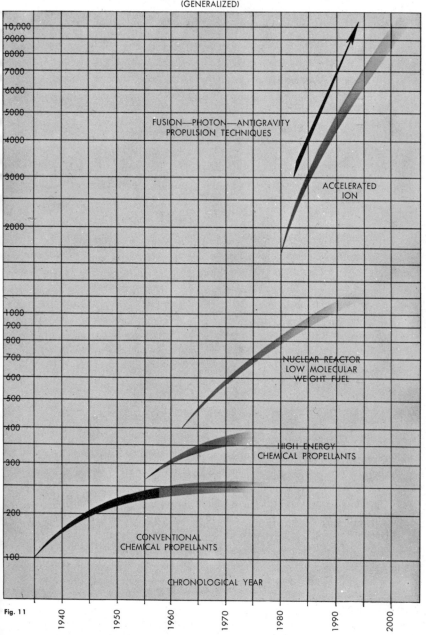

ONE-HUNDRED-YEAR PROGRESS
SPECIFIC IMPULSE SPECTRUM
(GENERALIZED)

FUSION—PHOTON—ANTIGRAVITY
PROPULSION TECHNIQUES

ACCELERATED
ION

NUCLEAR REACTOR
LOW MOLECULAR
WEIGHT FUEL

HIGH ENERGY
CHEMICAL PROPELLANTS

CONVENTIONAL
CHEMICAL PROPELLANTS

CHRONOLOGICAL YEAR

Fig. 11

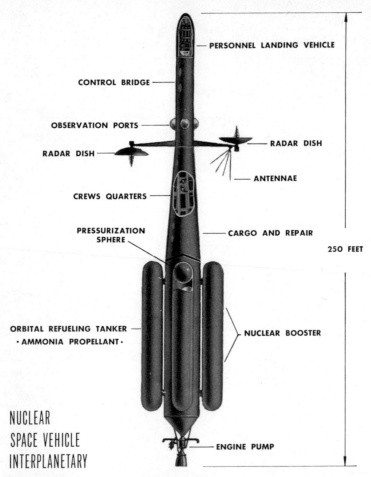

PERSONNEL LANDING VEHICLE

CONTROL BRIDGE

OBSERVATION PORTS

RADAR DISH

RADAR DISH

ANTENNAE

CREWS QUARTERS

PRESSURIZATION SPHERE

CARGO AND REPAIR

250 FEET

ORBITAL REFUELING TANKER
· AMMONIA PROPELLANT ·

NUCLEAR BOOSTER

NUCLEAR
SPACE VEHICLE
INTERPLANETARY

ENGINE PUMP

Fig. 12—This vehicle would be assembled in a satellite orbit around the Earth or the Moon. The main body of the vehicle consists of the nuclear rocket engine, propellant tankage, storage space and crews' work and flight areas.

Unmanned and disposable propellant tankers would be attached to the main body of the vehicle, the number of which would be dictated by flight requirements.

The personnel landing vehicle which is housed in the nose would make all flights between the target planet and the mother ship. The mother ship would await its smaller carrier in a terminal orbit around the subject planet.

order would be developed on the principle of free and equal, with the object of furthering scientific research and investigations. It seems to me that a development of this kind would dramatically emphasize the common heritage of humanity and would serve, perhaps significantly, to strengthen the sense of international community which is so vital to the development of a peaceful and secure world order."

The Problem of Innocent Passage in Space

The problems of space law are bound to be more complicated than those connected with the law of the high seas or of aviation law. A good example is the doctrine of "innocent passage" in international law, which protects ships that have strayed or have been blown into another nation's territorial waters, and permits them to leave without liability. It also protects ships entering the territorial waters of other nations on peaceful missions.

In 1919 this innocent passage doctrine was extended to aircraft, but the right was compromised later so that it became almost useless. The mass bombing raids over neutral countries dispelled what was left of the idea, so it was not incorporated into the Chicago Convention of 1944. With so many airplanes that drifted off course being shot down over the Iron Curtain during the current cold war, it can be concluded that this innocent passage of the sea doctrine does not pertain to aircraft on a worldwide scale.

It is significant to note, however, that soon after the launching of the first sputnik, Senator John Marshall Butler of Maryland strongly urged that it be shot down, thus denying the innocent passage of these first Earth satellites over our sovereign territory. But his request was ignored both on technical and political grounds.

This problem of innocent passage in space is now in the lap of the United Nations. It will have to seek an adequate solution, especially after the termination of the International Geophysical Year in 1958.

For example, although the nations of the world have tacitly agreed that the IGY satellites may proceed unquestioned around the Earth, the more serious question concerns the status of satellites and spaceships after the IGY is over.

Although the hour is growing late for reaching an international agreement on these matters before December 31, 1958, it is still not too late to take some concrete steps in solving the obvious first problems that will confront man and his instruments as he penetrates farther and farther into space. Even though we once thought of these problems as fantasy and "science fiction," we now realize that all humanity must look to the United Nations to take the lead in solving these urgent problems. The alternative is war that could conceivably destroy life on the Earth.

The Problem of Legal Space Regulations

Because missiles and space stations would be constantly changing positions, new legal regulations are needed to ensure the peaceful exploration and exploitation of space. Dr. C. Wilfred Jenks of England proposed eight such regulations which still need to be written and agreed upon by all the nations in a progressive series of steps. A large degree of international uniformity will be necessary in most of these eight rules or regulations to guarantee civilized activities in space and to keep space instrumentalities under proper control. Jenks' eight legal regulations would encompass the following:

1. Instrument-carrying missiles and satellites.
2. A navigation code in space.
3. A space radio-communication code.
4. Certification of space navigators and other space persons.
5. Rules governing construction of space stations, bases, etc.
6. A space rescue code.
7. Rules governing the carrying of passengers and goods.
8. Rules determining the application of the law to legal transactions occurring in space.

In preparing the foundations for an ultimate Space Law Code, we can learn much from the freedom of the seas maritime law, first established by the Dutch thinker, Hugo Grotius, the world's first great international lawyer, who founded this principle over four centuries ago.

There is even some ray of hope that the Soviet Union may agree to such United Nations regulation.

Shternfeld, a Soviet legal expert, wrote an interesting monograph in 1956, entitled, "To Whom Does Outer Space Belong?" in the *Iskusstvennue sputniki semli (Artificial Satellites of Earth)*. In his article he states: "The working out of international norms in the field of astronautics and the testing of superlong-range rockets must be carried out by the United Nations, according to the opinion of *Hester*, member of the British Astronomical Society, since it is doubtful that discussions conducted through usual diplomatic channels could give positive results." Hester brings forward the following:

1. The creation of a UN commission for co-ordination of scientific research in the field of astronautics.
2. Exchange of information by scientists and technicians.
3. Freedom of international projects and limitation of private initiative in the field of astronautics.
4. Control and co-ordination of tests, including the program of scheduled routes, speeds, time co-ordinates of takeoff, descent, etc.
5. Imposition of sanctions against states which violate agreements on the peaceful application of astronautics.

Shternfeld concludes, after apparently endorsing most of Hester's points, that these matters can be solved if there is "a positive approach by the negotiating parties and if artificial satellites are used only for peaceful purposes."

Foundations of a UN Space Force

After an examination of the basis for a United Nations space control theory, one is led to the conclusion that the international diplomats will soon foresee the need for the establishment of a UN Space Agency to enforce peace in outer space. An inter-

national space force, which could control and patrol the interplanetary regions in a fashion similar to modern science fiction
heroes, should be considered as part and parcel of any theories
of space control.

The precedent for the feasibility of such an international space
force has been the relative success of the recently organized first
true international police force, which has been operating on
the *ground* only in the disputed areas between Egypt and Israel.
To ensure mankind that any power-mad nation or nations in the
future do not usurp their free-space prerogatives in an abuse of
peaceful power privileges as envisioned by John Cobb Cooper,
then a UN Space Force will have to become organized. The UN
Space Force vehicles could be supplied by the major national
Earth powers, but the crews could be composed of space police-
navigators recruited from secondary or neutral United Nations
powers, much like the present UN Police Force. Space control
stations on Earth could also be supervised and monitored by
teams designated by the United Nations, even though con-
structed and owned by sovereign nations.

Without the establishment of a permanent UN Space Force,
in advance of any space dispute, then Andrew Haley's International Unanimity Theory, for instance, is in danger of being
compromised. To fill the vacuum of extralegal space control,
such a force-in-being should be considered along with the eight
steps toward an international legal space order that C. Wilfred
Jenks outlines. A ninth step, the establishment of an international Space Force, could monitor and provide space rescue,
space stations, space navigation assistance, among other duties.

Haley hints at the necessity of guaranteeing the joint world
ownership of space, which would justify a UN Space Force, in
the following apt phrase: "These principles must necessarily have
only interim application, for there must be a basic principle that
the regions beyond the aeropause may be *claimed by no nation*;
mankind may make only such utilization of space as will be for
the benefit of all mankind and to the detriment of no other intelligent creature." (Authors' italics.)

Stephen Decatur, over 150 years ago, established the basic

doctrine for the freedom of the seas, which provides an excellent analogy for extension to space law thinking today. "The Seas beyond reasonable coastal areas," he wrote, "are free and subject to control by no single despot or nation . . . [and] the sponsors of ships at sea must be responsible for the conduct of their vessels." This concept could be extended to apply to the justification for setting up a UN Space Force and a UN Space Law Code.

The expansion of the duties of the first international UN Police Force to include not only the Suez area but also the hotly disputed Gaza Strip and Sharm El Sheikh, which controls the mouth of the Gulf of Aqaba, points out the faith which the Free World has in such an organization. The extension of United Nations control to the upper-air and outer-space regions, with its own international air and space force, is a need which merits immediate consideration for initial planning purposes.

An international UN Space Force could be established in a series of steps, with an initially formed conventional air police force patrolling the no man's air over the Poles, Antarctica, the Arctic, the oceans and the uncivilized desert and jungle regions. The knowledge gained in this prior functioning would provide valuable professional insight into the greater problems that will be encountered as the Space Force extends its duties to the upper atmosphere and eventually to outer space.

The Problem of Establishing the UN Space Force

The organization, control, location, and types of vehicles in a UN Space Force present myriads of headaches for the branch of the United Nations Secretariat that will eventually be responsible for the administration of this new agency. However, none of these problems is insurmountable, and with the present machinery within the parent United Nations organization, they can be worked out in time. Let us look briefly at each of these four subordinate problem areas that are important to consider in the successful establishment of a UN Space Force.

Organization. Organization would be patterned after that of the temporary UN Police Force in the Near East. Canada's

Lester Bowles Pearson, former External Affairs Minister, who received the Nobel Peace Prize in 1957 for the role he played in creating this force, has suggested that a permanent force is needed. Such a permanent force, extended to include the keeping of the peace in space as well as on Earth, would require the official blessing and sanction of the U. S. Congress as well as the Supreme Soviet and other national governments. After such action is taken, then an organization can be set up with binational representation, under the General Assembly's jurisdiction but administered by the Secretariat.

Control. The control of such a UN Space Force would be lodged in the Assembly and its uses would not be subject to the veto of the Security Council. With its first commanders probably chosen from neutral nations or secondary powers, there would be a better chance of its being a success than if command control of the UN Space Force were vested in the hands of a representative of one of the superpowers. The spaceships, like the vehicles and supporting ground facilities, would probably be manned and produced by the big powers and then turned over to the United Nations for operational use under the UN flag. The pattern for this situation was established recently on a national scale within the United States Armed Forces when the Army, which had designed and produced the Jupiter IRBM, turned it over to the Air Force for operational purposes.

Location. The force could be dispersed on permanent Texas Tower-type launching platforms scattered in a balanced checkerboard pattern in international waters, so as not to endanger or annoy national populations. Elevated off the surface of the coastal international waters, these huge platforms, modeled after our present water-based radar picket outposts in the Atlantic and Pacific, will be able to handle at least several United Nations spaceships. The exhaust fumes on takeoff will be ejected downward through large holes in the floor of the ocean-based launch platforms, situated at strategic points all over the Earth.

UN Vehicle Requirements

One of the objectives of an embryonic UN Space Force is to develop recoverable rocket boosters—thus contributing to the economy of the overall operation. In addition, the first manned United Nations vehicles with international crews should have re-entry capabilities.

We are presupposing that with the establishment of a global UN Space Force all the support logistics will be favorable.

Typical Functions of UN Space Vehicles

The first manned UN space vehicles will probably assume patrol and reconnaissance duties for several days or weeks in their orbits around the Earth. After a reasonably short period spent in contiguous space surrounding the Earth, the space vehicles will re-enter the Earth's atmosphere and return to their base of operations.

Time, Space Control, and Survival

Andrew Haley, the president of the International Astronautical Federation, was not optimistic about the chances of calling a UN Space Code Convention in the near future. In an address in Los Angeles on November 16, 1957, he stated: "Mankind must mature appreciably to create an international authority having sole and complete jurisdiction over space flight and such an achievement must await the wise action of future generations." There is a question though as to whether we can afford to wait for future generations to draw up a comprehensive Space Law Code, because in the same speech Haley warned that "Technology has far outstripped the formulation of legal rules. *The gap has widened to the point that the peace of the world is threatened.*" (Authors' italics.)

Unfortunately, Dag Hammarskjöld, Secretary General of the United Nations, and his associates have shown no eagerness to take over the administration of outer space, or Antarctica. Their attitude is that they have problems enough in the inhabited

areas of the world. But in the fall of 1957 Hammarskjöld signified interest for the United Nations to establish a permanent,
standby United Nations Emergency Force (UNEF), similar to
the force now keeping the peace on the Israeli-Egyptian border,
and to be held ready for emergency duties. Such a proposal
evinced considerable support, but not action, as yet, but it is a
step in the right direction. Nevertheless, the United Nations
would welcome any agreement among rival claimants to space
that would outlaw these regions for warlike uses.

While the proposal for United Nations control of space appears to be logical, what happens when and if Russia or some
other nation deliberately tries to wreck all attempts to implement it? It seems to us that one point should be made clear: that
international space policing action should be carried out whether
Russia joins such action or not. We should be willing to furnish
superweapons and space vehicles to the United Nations and to
abide by the use of the UN Space Force as voted by the General
Assembly. Then if the Soviet Union tried obstruction or boy-
cott, it should be made clear that this is one program that the
world does not intend to be stopped by threats that any obstruc-
tionist nation might put forward. The ethical and moral pressures from the rest of the world should help to make such concerted action unanimous.

With the outlook extremely dim that the Security Council will
take the lead in the formulation of a United Nations sponsored
Space Law Code, due to the reluctance of the big power nations
to act on the subject, it appears that the initiative will have to
come from the General Assembly, where no veto is possible. A
hopeful note was sounded on December 8, 1957, just before the
end of the 1957 session of the Assembly, by its President, Sir
Leslie Munro, of New Zealand. He said that the General Assembly will have to consider control of sputniks and missiles
before the start of its regular session on September 16, 1958.
"The United Nations should show itself worthy of its responsibilities and control these new outer space developments," he
stated over a nationwide American television program. "If we
don't, then the world will go into its gravest peril."

chapter 14

the space world society and you

This is a time not of catastrophe but of choice, not of
disaster, but of decision.

Adlai Stevenson
Presbyterian Life—December 28, 1957

THE SPACE world culture of tomorrow will see the
possibilities of its peaceful fulfillment not in the unilateral advances of rocketry in one or two countries, but in a comprehensive and co-operative approach, where the spatial ends of rocketry's advances become a new global way of life.

Whichever course the nations of the world pursue in their
rocketry progress will bring about drastic changes in our society.
The price of transition into this new space world culture will
affect every institution as well as every individual in the United
States and the world. A considerable mass mobilization of the
world's best brains, labor, and raw materials appears to be part
of this transition, as well as other sacrifices that will have to be
made by all of the nations.

Some of the changes that will probably occur in our major
institutions will be examined from the broadest—the nation
and its destiny—to the narrowest—the individual and his job.
In a sort of inverted space world triangle, let us take a brief
sampling overview into eight major areas and institutions of our
society:

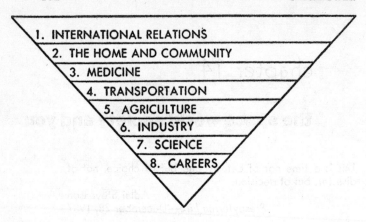

1. INTERNATIONAL RELATIONS
2. THE HOME AND COMMUNITY
3. MEDICINE
4. TRANSPORTATION
5. AGRICULTURE
6. INDUSTRY
7. SCIENCE
8. CAREERS

1. *International Relations*

The nations of the world will soon face three possible foreign policy alternatives as they cross the threshold of the Space Age into the new world culture of tomorrow. They can either: (1) sit back and ignore the march of technological progress and let "nature take its course," which is very risky to say the least as a rational alternative; or they can (2) pursue a fear complex pattern of spending twenty to forty billion dollars to "hide" from the specters of uncontrolled ICBM warfare and the annihilation of civilization; or they can (3) face up to the problem and invest their billions positively in a constructive international space program, where the fear of mutual H-bomb annihilation will be erased forever from men's minds.

If the second alternative is pursued (the building of shelters for protection against the H-bomb and mass fallout), little money will be left to undertake the third, either on a single national scale or as part of an international effort. The tremendous and wasteful expenditures for burrowing underground to provide populations with tenuous protective shelters is both an expensive and questionable solution. How many peoples of a large metropolis like New York would be able to get safely into such

H-bomb-proof shelters either in or out of the city? Ten percent? Maybe only five percent?

A civil defense expert sometime back estimated reliably that less than one to three percent of the populace of the largest metropolis could escape from the city before an H-bomb hit, if they had only a half-hour warning. And even then, many of those who were lucky enough to get out would be mowed down by delayed radioactive effects.

The same analogy holds true for putting factories underground and trying to store millions of tons of food against some future military thermonuclear catastrophe. The astronomical cost of such enterprises does not make sense while there are millions starving in the underdeveloped nations of the world.

The foreign policies of the major powers of the world in the Space Age will have to take into recognition the stark fact that other nations, large or small, should be treated as equals and not as inferiors. This new shift toward mutual world understanding, instead of the present mere tolerance on the part of the superpowers toward their less potent fellow members, should do much toward helping to create better harmony in the halls of the United Nations.

To supplement this dynamic new approach to foreign policy, an international cultural exchange program would help gain momentum for the Space Age, aided no doubt by inexpensive rocket trips for students and scholars from various points on the world's map. Such an exchange could be highlighted by semi-annual cultural and scientific congresses to be held on a rotating basis, which would encourage a better appreciation of the arts and sciences. As a parallel to these programs, there should be an increase in the output of the national and international information agencies, with a stepped-up exchange of books, films, recordings, etc., in all the major spoken languages.

A sense of urgency in educating the world to the concept that space flight and space control are not the concern of one or two countries alone is very important at this time. The social compression of the Earth which will result from the fantastic speeds of rockets will revolutionize our world cultures more than any other single event since the Industrial Revolution. The amalgamation of all the peoples of the world under the jurisdiction of the United Nations should result in a modern Pax Romana of global political unity that should bring new political and civil freedoms for the peoples of the world.

With new concepts of human relations that will evolve in the space world, new techniques and approaches to problems in space might be successfully applied back here on Earth. For instance, we may assume there will be no national or international farmers' lobby hindering the development of hydroponics (farming by water) on the Moon or Mars, like the one on Earth that caused restrictions to be placed on the marketing of oleomargarine for so many years.

The steps taken at the December, 1957, NATO Conference in creating a scientific committee to start pooling Western scientific resources, and the statements of intention to consult more fully through the NATO Council were healthy signs. The need for integrating and standardizing Western military IRBM production, operations and logistics support provides a realistic analogy and practical working experience for a similar step in international space-flight co-operation. This co-operation on the military level could be extended to the peaceful, scientific level. Adlai Stevenson recently stated that there is a great opportunity now "to go beyond the everlasting chatter about arms." One way or another the world must meet the Space Age challenge.

2. The Home and Community

Florida and California, two of the fastest growing states in the United States, can attribute much of their fantastic growth to the impact of rockets and missiles. The new boomtowns of Cocoa and Orlando in Florida, the former being the home of world-famed Cape Canaveral Air Force Missile Test Center; Point Mugu, Camp Cooke, San Diego, and Los Angeles in California; Denver, Colorado; the rocket and aircraft cities in Texas; and "Rocket City, U.S.A." at Huntsville, Alabama are but a few of the cities and towns that have been revolutionized and expanded beyond their limits by the rocket industry. Led by the missilemen, who breathe the lore of the latest state-of-the-art in missilery, new types of people populate these space communities on Earth. In many cases, they are found exercising their citizens' rights as community leaders in their off-duty or nonworking hours.

The family will undergo great changes in the forthcoming Space Age. It is still too early to predict many of the important changes that will take place within the home. With a more mobile society, different members of the family may find themselves working on the opposite sides of the Earth—or in space; and, eventually, children will be born in space or on some far-off planet, and may never see the Earth for an entire lifetime— even though their parents were born on this planet. Visiting relatives or friends in the space world of tomorrow could conceivably entail long trips—of several million miles—to arrive at their abodes.

3. Medicine

The health of the peoples of the space world may be greatly affected by new advances in medicine. Besides space medical and biological research, practical medicine may benefit from space flight in many unsuspected ways. For instance, weightlessness, which at first may be a nuisance to space navigators, may be the therapy for some nervous disorders and even for organic ailments.

Medicine in space may also benefit from controlled solar and cosmic radiation. Thus, radiation therapy may become a medical blessing in disguise to surgeons practicing in an orbit at 2,000 miles above the Earth. The space doctors of the future may very well find new challenges and careers in the medical profession.

4. *Transportation*

No longer will there be Sunday afternoon traffic jams or sub-way rush hours to cope with in the world of tomorrow. Fast rocket-propelled helicopters, rocket trains and rocket-powered cars will whirl the busy white-collar commuter out to the suburbs in five or ten minutes, or less. The suburbs will be extended far out into the country by 1975, so that it will probably be fashionable to live a hundred miles or more away from a big metropolis. Traveling either on or close to the ground at speeds faster than the present-day supersonic rocket sleds at Holloman Air Development Center, Albuquerque, New Mexico, will help to revolutionize society.

In addition to this fast surface or close-to-the-surface transportation, hypersonic interstate and international rocket transporation fleets will whisk vacationers and workers all over the world in a matter of a few hours at the most. These commercial vehicles will be electronically controlled through intricate safety mechanisms that will prevent tragic space crashes from ever occurring during their brief missions.

Mail service will be improved around the world, with the aid of rocket-propelled monorail service on land, and rocket-powered catamaran boats that will literally fly along either on or close to the surface of the water.

Privately owned individual or family-style rocketships to be used for going on "weekends to the Moon" will undoubtedly have to await new exotic rocket-propulsion breakthroughs as well as advances in guidance—so you won't end up on Jupiter by mistake.

5. *Agriculture*

The farmer's number-one headache in the past has been the vagaries of the weather. If he were only in a position to predict the best times of the year to sow the seeds, or if he could accurately forecast droughts, freezes, floods, or hurricanes, then he would save himself and the consumer billions of dollars annually.

But until we can extend our present short-range weather fore-casting through the media of weather reconnaissance satellites, and eventually with weather-control space vehicles, the farmer is still subject to the whims of nature. The agricultural economy of all nations and peoples would greatly benefit from such scientific advances as space weather forecasting around the Earth.

6. Industry

A clue to some of the major changes which are already taking place in many United States industries, particularly the aircraft industry, is the shift to missiles. The transition into these new products is causing painful readjustments on the part of many industries. With five percent of the defense budget of the fiscal year, 1959, being allocated for missiles (including procurement and development), and serving as a warning signal of things to come, one can surmise that this percentage will jump tremendously during the next decade. The missile industry is in reality a complex of many different types of industries that cut across all segments of American life and technical know-how. New amalgamations of propulsion and fuel industries as well as airframe and electronics industries have already taken place, and will continue to accelerate in the future.

The shift that is occurring now is not only being felt by the larger prime contractor aircraft industries, but also the important subcontractors in electronic and propulsion components as well. In addition, new, smaller, all-missile industries are sprouting up all over the landscape. And the Big Three of the automotive concerns already have a substantial foot in the door in this new multibillion-dollar enterprise. Chrysler is the prime contractor on the Army's Jupiter, Ford is heavily invested in Aeroneutronics, which launched the Far Side Project balloon rockets, and General Motors is deeply involved in the IRBM-ICBM program through its A-C Spark Plug guidance packages.

The rocket-propulsion industry of tomorrow will expand to encompass the newer exotic propulsion fields, such as nuclear, ion, and photon. Entirely new companies will be formed to com-

pete with the older established ones in the more conventional
liquid and solid chemical propulsion areas. Meanwhile, the present-day giant jet engine companies may find themselves turning
out thousands of recoverable and nonrecoverable rocket boosters
of all shapes and sizes. Closely allied to the engine industry is the
chemical industry. The new boron hydrazine and nitric acid industries are already expanding rapidly.

The airframe industries, in addition to conversion to missile
structures and space vehicle configurations, will probably spread
out into designing and building air-conditioned space cabins,
based on their experience in producing pressurized cabins for
today's giant airliners.

The rubber and textile industries will probably both be loaded
down with heavy orders in the spacesuit business, civilian and
military, as more and more men and women become engaged
in ventures into space.

The mining industry will dig down farther into the earth to
help lift man farther out into space. For instance, one of the
alkali metals, cesium, can be used in a liquid form as an ultra-
energy fuel for an ion engine. It is believed that a cesium-fuel-
powered missile may reach velocities of 100,000 miles per hour
in space.

The missile and missile ground support industry will multiply
in its needs and products. Huge gantry cranes and massive con-
crete-and-steel launch platforms will provide lucrative contracts
for the giant steel and fabricating industries. Contracting firms
will provide service similar to that of the World War II teams at
most of the Pacific islands, or comparable to the project of con-
structing the Distant Early Warning (DEW) Line and missile
test facilities.

The optical and camera industries will benefit from the demands for large high-speed, missile-tracking cameras. The electronics industry will probably increase the fastest in terms of
sheer demand for its products, from giant radars to miniature
transistor tubes. More and bigger electronic computers and instrumentation panels will require an increase in skilled manpower to manufacture, design, and maintain them. The radio

industry will mushroom, particularly in the newer fringe aspects of minitrack and microlock tracking stations and radio telescopic receivers and telemetering transmitters.

All sorts of supplemental flight gear needed by the larger companies will be turned out by the small business suppliers who are in a unique position to make a worthwhile contribution to the cause of space flight. Such examples as fuel and oxidizer valves, turbopumps, explosive bolts, flanges, fuses, wires, pipes, protective fiber and asbestos linings all play their essential parts in launching a huge rocket. The manufacturers of these items are just as important in their contributions to the overall success and effectiveness of missile-launching efforts as are the rocket- and missilemen themselves.

Consulting and research in the field of interplanetary travel, including environmental measurements, will bring about the growth of many new concerns whose main purpose will be to advise the major space-vehicle industries.

Nontechnical white-collar industries, such as manufacturers of space toys, will boom. It is fairly obvious that there will be no need for new- and used-car salesmen on the Moon or the planets, but real-estate promoters may be able to open up new astronomical sales vistas through the Mars and Saturn divisions of some future "Outer-Space Development Corporation."

The commuting metropolitan businessman will be affected in many indirect and direct ways by the changes brought about in the above-mentioned "space industries of tomorrow." But it is more difficult to foresee the specific changes in white-collar, business, or professional lives than it is to project the more obvious changes in the missile industries themselves. The theater and the arts will look toward space for their themes. Space bookstores should flourish.

New industrial inventions will also revolutionize our lives. For instance, new findings on the properties of chlorophyl will make possible new foods, better energy-conductor sources and a carbon-dioxide absorber for use by spacemen. In another area, we can envision small, packaged, portable nuclear reactors which can be transported to the Moon and to the planets to supply economical power for space stations there.

In conclusion, let us remember that for every man who is sent into space, industry will have to have thousands working on various materials to get him out there safely and to return him to Earth.

7. Science

Society in the Space Age will probably see a balance among the primary and secondary national powers on leadership in applied science and engineering, as well as in the complex forms of industrial production. The Swiss, for instance, who are world renowned for their fine watches, may provide future leadership in the miniaturization of intricate guidance and electronic components for space vehicles.

The future need for a permanent peaceful international space program to help guarantee full employment and to stabilize the rocket and missile industries will ensure that any future international work projects will be channeled into a constructive space effort. In this way, the unfortunate present-day cyclical fluctuations in the aircraft and missile industries, with their attendant wastes in manpower and money, will be alleviated. For space flight is too big a proposition for any one country, military service, or company to obtain a monopoly.

Rather, a pooling of each country's knowledge in the field of rocketry is an apparent necessity to prevent duplication of effort and to cut down on the heavy costs involved. This concept can be extended to the international level, where the first steps to pool the atomic energy knowledge of the West were taken after sputnik. President Eisenhower's proposed Science for Peace program modeled after the successful United Nations Atoms for Peace plan is another step in this direction.

8. New Space Careers

A whole new span of professional and skilled Space Age careers are evolving both in civilian and military life. These astronautical careers run the gamut from cyrogenics to astromedicine. Some of the more significant ones will be discussed for the benefit of both young people and parents who are seriously interested in keeping in step with the Space Age by advising their off-spring to pursue a new career discipline. They are listed in the order of their importance and future growth potential.

Rocket Propulsion. In this fast-growing field, all sorts of engineers are needed, especially in the nuclear and exotic fuels areas. Thermodynamics specialists and ceramics experts are urgently needed to help perfect the rocket engines and thrust chambers of the future. Experts are needed in the relatively younger solid-fuel-development fields as well as the better established hydrocarbon, liquid-propellant fuel technologies. The frontiers of ion and photon propulsion offer new areas where the professional propulsion expert will join forces with the electronic specialist in a new amalgamated discipline . . . as yet unnamed.

Astroelectronics. In this new profession that relies heavily on electrical engineering for a basic background, new disciplines of missile guidance (gyroscope, autopilot, and timer servomechanism specialists), electronic computer specialists (both ground- and space-borne), and telemetry instrumentation experts have grown fast, and will continue to expand rapidly. Propulsion, and missile guidance and control are probably the two most crucial professional realms that will lead the movement into space. The fantastic new frontiers of radar development, installations and tracking facilities have created thousands of new jobs for experts in this essential electronic Space Age profession. Miniaturization and transistor techniques will be needed in great abundance, which should open up thousands of new job opportunities for women who appear to have a special knack for this type of work.

Astronautical Structures. This new profession is a developmental offshoot of the present aerodynamics and mechanical engineering fields. It encompasses such engineering specialties as weight systems, ground-support equipment, flight structures, missile design and configurations, metal alloy techniques, ceramic nose cone specialists, etc.

In addition to the foreground basic careers directly connected with the missile and space-flight industries, in the technical and scientific fields, there are new extensions of allied professions which will all be necessary in a balanced panorama of jobs for the space-flight programs of tomorrow.

Some of those equally important careers, which are either directly or indirectly connected with space development, are as follows:

Space Medicine. This profession already has a great tradition based on the pioneering work of Dr. Hubertus Strughold of the Air Force School of Aviation Medicine in Texas, of Col. John Stapp, for his supersonic centrifuges and rocket sleds, and Maj. David Simons, for his extended 20-mile "Man High" balloon flights on the fringes of space. These pioneering doctors who are experimenting with the problems of sending men into space for long periods are doing a yeoman job to break through the unknown barriers that might halt man's physical and psychological progress into space, even though he might already have conquered the mechanical problems.

Astrophysics. In this extension of pure physics out beyond the confines of the atmosphere, such pioneers as Dr. Joseph Kaplan, head of the U. S. National Committee for the IGY, and Dr. S. Fred Singer, Associate Professor of Physics at the University of Maryland, have been making significant experiments in searching out the unknowns in cosmic rays, the aurora, ultraviolet rays, X-rays, the Earth's oblateness, and meteoric dust. The knowledge gained from these studies will be an invaluable boon to the future of man. It offers a fruitful future to the serious-minded scientists of tomorrow.

Other Space Professions. In addition to those professions mentioned previously, new fields, such as astromathematics, quantum mechanics, space sociology, space anthropology, astronomy, space law, and space teaching will expand. Most of those in the last-named field will not be "pure" space teachers as far as their knowledge and background are concerned, but will probably integrate special up-to-date knowledge about space advances into their traditional subject matter or area specialties.

To prepare our youth for these new space world careers will require an overhauling of the educational system from kindergarten through graduate school. Therefore we must next examine the American educational system, with particular attention to changes needed to help the people survive in the space world of tomorrow.

chapter 15

education for the space world of tomorrow

Students going into scientific fields can be pioneers today
in the . . . unmapped world of science. . . . Enough remains to be discovered and mapped to guarantee excite-
ment and venture to more young scientists and engineers
than we are likely to have for many years to come.

Rear Adm. Hyman Rickover
Chief, Naval Reactors Branch
Atomic Energy Commission
On the "See It Now" television program—January, 1958

Tʜᴇ Earth satellites are a symbolic challenge to a
new way of life. The anxieties and problems that have arisen in
the aftermath of the sputniks have created an atmosphere where
parents and educators have begun a wholehearted and serious
soul-searching into the inadequacies of our American educational system. For the full flowering of *spacepower* tomorrow,
insofar as the United States is concerned, depends mainly on the
health of our schools. A sound educational program geared to
the necessities of the *Space Age* will guarantee more than any
other factor the continued leadership of the United States as a
world power.

The questions and alarms concerning the deficiencies in the
school system have multiplied intensely. A school system that
turns out only three engineers and scientists for every hundred
pupils who enter grade school requires a tremendous re-evaluation.

What are some of the possible changes that the new "Space Age awareness" will bring about in the education of our youth? What sort of curriculum can our present twelve-year-old Johnny and Suzy Smith look forward to in the high schools, military academies, and colleges of tomorrow? Will one-year-old Bobby and Patsy Brown be able to look forward to a longer school year? How about the college outlook of Sammy Jones and Gloria Green in the Space Age? What careers should they be pursuing so that they can keep in step with the times and not be left behind? How will we pay for Space Age education? What changes will face the military educational system? These are but some of the many questions that face the different age levels of youth today and also their parents in attempting to ascertain the hopes and prospects for the future.

An examination of a few of the areas of education that will be affected by this whirling phenomenon will give us a glimpse of schools in the year 2000 and beyond.

Aims of Space Age Education

Today's younger generation is expected to have a life span of at least seventy-five years. If that is so, today's children will live at least to the year 2035. One of the more important conditions they must then learn to live "with" and "in" is "space." These boys and girls will be our space citizens and pioneers. By the year 2000 the Moon probably will have been explored and Venus and Mars will have been probed. Man should be living in orbit between Earth and Moon, and space will be his home.

In the year 2000, man will have experienced speeds up to 50,000 miles per hour. The Moon itself will be less than four days away—less than today's coast-to-coast travel by automobile, or boat voyage to Europe. Such speeds should make any spot on Earth commutable in a fraction of an hour. Thus your children "may" be working halfway around the world and be able to come home to dinner. With a shrunken Earth, we must become world citizens. In spite of our differences, the Earth must, and will, be forced to unite.

EDUCATION FOR THE SPACE WORLD OF TOMORROW   197

In an October 14, 1957, report to the President of the United States on space flight, the American Rocket Society stressed the nebulous benefits of a comprehensive space program in these words: "The explorations of Columbus were justified in prospect by a 'short route' to the Indies. They were justified in terms of the times by Inca and Aztec gold, a wholly unforeseen dividend. Today, both of these short term goals are seen to be miniscule in terms of the ultimate results." The true aims of Space Age education should stress both short- and long-range goals. But it should not be blinded by the immediate goals; otherwise the more important long-range ones will be soon forgotten. Long-range educational goals should be compatible with those of the United Nations, as well as of this country itself. The goals should also be geared to the plans and problems of space flight in the future. The chief purpose of Space Age education should be knowledge and not mere social adjustment—with children having an equal opportunity to develop their talents for the future.

Prospects of a Space Age Curriculum

Recently, a typical American midwestern school teacher was overheard to remark, "We've gone through all the ages, including the Space Age and now, thank God, that's over!" This teacher, along with thousands of others, is under a delusion about Space Age education's being "over." In reality, it is just beginning to show some signs of effectiveness in the many schools where it is encouraged.

Thus, we should prepare our children for their adult years in A.D. 2000, with a new emphasis in education.

On the preschool level, children's reading books, picture books, music, and games, with basic Space Age material and terminology, should be made available to parents, nursery school, and kindergarten teachers. Preparatory material should not be only on the scientific aspect of the Space Age, but should also emphasize the studies of children and cultures in other lands: for example, "How do they say 'Hello' in any other language?"

On the elementary school level, teaching aids in all subjects should include Space Age material. Some farsighted leaders have already begun to add such material to the curriculums. From the first grade on, reading textbooks should include space stories; spelling books, new words such as "thrust" and "specific impulse"; and arithmetic books, problems and mathematical symbols relating to the Space Age. Science units should be given greater emphasis, introducing terminology and basic understandings that children will be living with as adults in the Space Age. Social study units should be broadened in their aspects. Transportation units should include study of spaceships and other space vehicles, and languages should be introduced, not as experiments, but as a permanent part of the curriculum on the elementary level.

On the high-school and college level, astronomy, astronautics, mathematics and physics should be required in the curriculums. In a shrunken world we must also be better acquainted with peoples. Therefore, we should emphasize more, and in some cases, require the study of languages, world history, sociology, comparative religions, comparative literature, world cultures, and anthropology.

With the interest of youth in space and rocketry helping to turn the attention of the adult public to the exciting new realms of space travel, there is every expectation that new impetus will be given to basic research in the high schools as well as in government, college and industrial research laboratories. Youth's yearning to probe into the unknown will lead to basic rocketry courses in high-school chemistry and physics classes. Already many communities and high schools have set up rocket clubs, under proper supervision, to conduct experiments in this new frontier of knowledge. The new emphasis on basic research, starting in the high schools, has added a new zest to the whole missile and satellite program.

Education in the Space Age does not mean a drastic reversal of the pattern of operating our schools, with round-the-clock sessions twelve months of the year. Although physics and chemistry will be encouraged more, it will not mean that these subjects will be compulsory for *all* students. Students and teachers will still have their traditional summer vacations and weekends off, although there will be a swing toward a better use of these traditional "rest" periods, with an increased emphasis on school camping, both during the regular school year and during the summers. These public camps will combine work and play by integrating the formal school curriculum subjects into the informal camp atmosphere, where the students may very well become inspired to pursue new careers that they might not otherwise have found interesting.

In order to meet these requirements, school attendance years must be extended all the way into college, with at least two years required of everyone. We can afford more school years, since we all have more years to live, work, and play.

Although the more generalized Space Age knowledge at this time can be taught within the confines of the present traditional course, there are additional steps which can and should be taken to enrich the more formal curriculum.

Suggested Steps in Space-Age Education

The following suggestions are not listed in any particular sequence in order of importance:

Science Fiction in the Schools

Adapting science fiction literature to the schools has tremendous possibilities for motivating students to look into the future of the Universe. Good science fiction stories, both at the teen-age and the adult level, is a healthful and worthwhile stimulant for real scientific pursuits.

A Space Age Weekly

There is also a need for mass appeal through Space Age periodicals geared predominantly to the youth of America and written in their language. A *Space Age Weekly* could adequately supplement the present high-school political science and literary subscription papers and periodicals, such as *The Weekly News Review*, the *Scholastic* magazines, *American Observer*, etc., or be included as subsections of these worthwhile periodicals.

Space Comics

Space comics should come into their own again as a means of interesting youth in the prospects of the future. Buck Rogers, the recognized comic strip of the future, which was so popular in the thirties, is being revived in dozens of newspapers with a new episode that started on January 13, 1958. The first new Buck Rogers theme was centered around the problem of whether Buck would find the missing satellite in the third ring of Saturn!

It would not be surprising to see Steve Canyon and Terry and the Pirates converting to a U. S. or UN Space Force in their adventures, which are followed avidly by millions. Neither would it be surprising to see a revived Flash Gordon, providing a welcome medium to educate children about the complexities of the Space Age.

Space Youth Groups

Other immediate channels for space world preparation may be opened through youth organizations, such as the Boy Scouts and Girl Scouts. Boys and girls could be trained in the fundamentals of space navigation, for instance, in a Space Scouts group, but these future leaders should be trained by professional people.

A similar program of preparation could be introduced into the Boys' Clubs of America and Police Athletic Leagues. The Future Farmers of America could be introduced to hydroponics or other advanced techniques for farming on an overpopulated Earth or on any dry celestial body which we may reach.

Space-Flight Derby

Another source of training might be a space-flight derby sponsored by newspapers, colleges, nations, or the United Nations to encourage new design and hardware for rockets or spaceships. Special monetary or other type awards could be given to the winners. Control through organizations will help prevent accidents, and safety standards should be set up and publicized.

An International Educational Exchange Program

An increased exchange of scientists and engineers as well as science students at college level should be undertaken as a permanent program. The initiation of this program under the Fulbright Act, and more recently in the NATO area, should be drastically expanded.

A Space Academy

There is an immediate need to establish a national, and an international, Space Academy. An institution of this kind would be nonmilitary in its scope, emphasizing rather the biological, physical, political, and technical problems of space flight. It would be open to both sexes and would offer career opportunities on both the undergraduate and graduate levels in various aspects of space flight.

Space Field Trips

A less immediate step, but one well worth looking forward to, will be educational field trips by rocket or hypersonic jet plane. School children and teachers will be able to study foreign peoples and their customs on the spot. This method of increasing world understanding, through the help of the space medium, would tend to place a greater emphasis on geography, sociology, anthropology, economics, and political science in the school curriculum than formerly noted.

Funding for Space Age Education

The price of existence in the space world is going to come quite high for all nations. With the Soviets investing some $4,500,-000,000 in science alone in the near future, the United States is challenged to do the same, and more.

The National Education Association on December 20, 1957, came out with a new call for an expanded five-year Federal aid program totaling $4,600,000,000. This call for money was for teachers' salaries as well as for new schools and was a new step taken by the NEA over its previous request for temporary emergency money for school construction only.

With the realization that the key to improved scientific advances lay in smaller classes, with more adequate counseling of the gifted children, more attention to individual differences, and the offering of science scholarships, such a plan was obvious. No attempt was made to project this plan beyond a five-year estimate, but the proponents, including Dr. William G. Carr, executive secretary of the NEA, admit it is to be a permanent program. Would it be unfair to estimate that such a "permanent" plan might set its sights on an $8,000,000,000 annual Federal outlay for public schools in five years with an increase to $15,000,000,-000 in ten years? If the present world conditions require "bold answers" as Dr. Carr, and Dr. James L. McCaskill, the NEA's legislative director, intimate, then such figures are not unrealistic. To meet the educational challenge ahead requires that renewed public interest in the schools and colleges be met with concrete and massive support from the one agency that can provide it—the Federal Government. With the cost factor being the chief deterrent to the improved quality of the system, the barrier must be broken through on all levels—local, state, and national, particularly the latter.

Additional money is needed to provide scholarships, especially in scientific fields, for those in the top third of the talented youth who cannot go to college because of lack of funds. Financial aid to states to strengthen the teaching of science, for the purchasing of laboratory equipment, and for aiding teachers and students in graduate study is a must. Good science teachers are the key to inspire students to pursue careers in science. Without these, many potential future engineers and mathematicians will choose some other life endeavor.

It must also be considered that a Federal financial "shot in the arm" to the educational system could tend to unbalance the curriculum in the schools by insisting on an overemphasis of science at the expense of the rest of the subject matter via the "Washington purse string." A well-balanced curriculum is necessary to ensure that the young people become well-rounded, responsible citizens of a dynamic democracy. We cannot afford to have them turned out as technical specialists only, to help win a technological race, but must insist on their being socially minded and culturally adapted to the changes in the world. With this approach, we may feel assured that these young people may put their newly acquired scientific knowledge to proper use.

We must also keep in mind that not all of our youth will have a natural bent for technical matters and that certainly an equal number, if not a majority, will render their services in fields of government, politics, economics, history, psychology, languages, finance, business management, music, art, and other fields. Albeit, the liberal arts student, although not a technical specialist, must learn about the Universe and must know space terminology if he is to satisfy the cultural needs of our time.

In order to educate an expanding world population, we shall have to build more colleges as well as expand elementary and high schools. A survey should be started now to prepare for increased population and space world curriculum.

On December 30, 1957, the Administration unveiled a four-year, $1,000,000,000 Federal emergency program designed to eliminate deficiencies in the nation's educational system, which if "allowed to continue, could seriously weaken our security effort." The plan, proposed by the Secretary of Health, Education, and Welfare, Marion Folsom, and endorsed by President Eisenhower, would establish 40,000 federally financed college scholarships over a four-year-period, with preference given to students with good preparation in science and mathematics. The Secretary also proposed some 5,500 graduate fellowships and lesser amounts of money for guidance and counseling, and matching grants to the states for improved student testing techniques.

Unfortunately, this proposal tries to cure the basic ill in our educational system by trying to cover the sore on the surface. No money was allocated for new school buildings or for across-the-board boosts in teachers' salaries, which is the necessary foundation to make the other plan workable.

This program appears to be too inadequate in its attempts to rectify a big problem that requires a massive approach to its ultimate solution. However, perhaps it is a beginning which will lead to a new expansiveness in the educational system. The time has come for the communities, states, and special interest groups to compromise their fears of Federal control in the interests of the need for national educational funding.

Finding Space Age Teachers

There appears to be a serious problem in finding effective Space Age teachers in the quantity and quality needed. To supplement those few teachers who are "space-minded" through personal interest, a massive teacher-training program for the Space Age is needed. The best, most economical, and fastest method to accomplish this end is for the various colleges of education, State teachers colleges, State departments of education, and local school systems to conduct Space Age education workshops not only during the regular school terms but in the summer as well. Space Age scholarships provided by the aviation and missile industries would be an excellent incentive for teachers.

At present, professional people from industry, college, and the Government should be enlisted to train leaders and to write textbooks for the new era. In the future, the major bulk of the new teachers and leaders can be expected to be products of the space world college curriculums, but they should also be required to spend some time in industry and government in order to keep their courses abreast of industrial and politico-military advances in space.

Military Education in the Space World

We shall limit the major scope of our analysis of military education in the space world to the three undergraduate service academies (the Naval Academy, Military Academy, and Air Force Academy) and their curriculums, since it is in these institutions that the greatest adjustment to the revolution of missile technology and to a probably single-service educational system *can* and *must* be made.

The Curriculums at the Three Academies

At present each academy gives its students a basic grounding in fundamentals of general education. Much of the curriculum of the new Air Force Academy has been "borrowed heavily" from West Point's four-year cadet program. The emphasis on English and the humanities, American and world history, geography, philosophy, psychology, economics, American Government, chemistry, physics, mathematics, a foreign language, and international relations are fundamental core courses in all three academies.

The Air Force Academy, West Point, and Annapolis differ in their curriculums in the areas of *technical* specialties pertaining to their peculiar branch of the service. In the Air Force Academy for instance, electrical engineering, mechanics and materials (relating to aircraft) appear in the third year, and thermodynamics, aircraft design and aerodynamics in the fourth year. In the Naval and Military Academies, similar courses are given in the latter two years for cadets specializing in Army and Navy careers. At West Point in the third and fourth years, the cadets specialize in the fields of chemistry, engineering, electronics and mechanics, but *only* as these apply to the Army and the weapons technology of that service.

The balance between scientific and social-humanistic areas of learning would remain roughly the same under a Space Age undergraduate educational setup. A broadening of the scientific areas, to include basic insights into the other services' technical problems, would be balanced with a similar broadening in the humanities area, placing greater emphasis on human relations and on understanding of world affairs as a result of the international impact of missiles.

Advantages of Updating Service Academy Curriculums

A single Space Age military service would establish a new requirement for all officers. For the first time in the history of the United States, it will need a multitude of triple threat commanders capable of wearing three hats. Future leaders are needed who can make critical, split-second decisions based on fingertip knowledge of the capabilities of all forces under them—land, sea, air, and space. The time to start making preparations to educate these future leaders of a U. S. Armed Force is now, so that they will be ready to adjust to the new, reorganized, truly unified military service when they graduate as a second lieutenant or ensign. This problem holds true not only for the student cadets and midshipmen in the three service academies, but also for the thousands of Reserve Officers Training Corps cadets on the various college campuses and for the men in Officer Candidate School. Lead time is just as important in the education of our future military leaders as it is for producing bombers or intercontinental ballistic missiles or spaceships which these men may employ someday.

We do not propose to explore the mechanics of how this particular integration will take place. These steps can be handled adequately by the commandants and deans and their staffs at the respective academies and schools. This matter will be relatively simple, once decisions are made. Rather we would emphasize the emergency and urgency of the long lead time needed to accomplish the ends desired. That is why the present time is so critical to take the first steps toward true military educational integration.

Other advantages of an officer education program under a single-service system are as follows:

It would help to eliminate the overlapping of responsibility, and also help to clarify the roles, strategy, and missions of land, sea, and air, particularly as they relate to the missiles.

It would tend to ease the friction between branches of the Armed Forces on employment of missiles. General Nathan Twining recently stated that pushbutton missiles are taking the glamour and romance out of flying, so concentration on the art and science of missilery in the last two years of all three service academies' curriculums could replace this lost romance.

Better control through more standardization of the curriculums would result. The current defense doctrine would be taught, which would guarantee a more unified strategy for employment of all military forces.

An exchange of professional technical knowledge among the staffs of the three undergraduate academies could take place more readily and with better results.

A closer co-ordination with the graduate professional military education programs would also result from such a move on the undergraduate level. Since the Air University, Army Command and General Staff College, Naval War College, Army War College, Armed Forces Staff College and the National War College already possess interservice students in their schools and liaison representatives on their faculties to observe and to lecture on missions of their respective services, the problem of a more unified curriculum would appear to be less intense at this level.

The United States could still keep the three physical locations of the present academies for geographic dispersal purposes as well as to ensure that at least ten percent of the total of our future professional officers will be coming from them. We shall also have to rely on a continuing output of the ROTC officers who are trained in civilian colleges.

General Thomas D. White, Chief of Staff of the Air Force, spoke on unification to a gathering of aviation writers in San Francisco in 1956. His statesmanlike words seem to provide an excellent guideline for the makers of space cirriculum at the service academies, for he said, "Toward this end, I believe our military services will move toward more complete unification.

We need a military organization that will help us to be free of conflicting service loyalties and confusing influences.

"One step would be to more closely integrate existing forces. The Continental Air Defense Command is an example of what I mean. Units of the Army, Navy, and Air Force are united in a common effort—the air defense of the United States. Further integration of our forces into joint commands oriented toward one mission might be effective.

"Another step toward more complete unification would be the free transfer of men between the services. Perhaps this would allow the men in each of the three services to think a little more objectively about the requirements of defense and less about gaining or keeping of weapons and missions for their own particular branch.

"With the passing of time, the roles and missions of all services seem to overlap more and more. Conceivably if these trends continue, the day could come when, for all practicable purposes, all three services would have the same weapons, the same capabilities, the same limitations, and all attempting to do the same jobs. If that happens, perhaps we certainly would find it advisable to standardize uniforms and streamline the organization."

The future officer of the U. S. Armed Force of tomorrow can well ponder these prophetic words as he prepares for leadership in defense of the nation—a defense that obviously will be geared around missiles and satellites—for both offensive and defensive strategy and tactics. His basic officer education should reflect this coming change.

Instead of adding light plane pilot training only to the Air Force Academy curriculum, visits should be made to the Air Force Missile Test Center, Redstone Arsenal, Point Mugu, Patrick Air Force Base, and Camp Cooke, California, where the cadets can get firsthand briefings and observations of the missile weapons systems which they will be commanding later.

New military careers in missile engineering, maintenance, support, command, and employment are opening up new vistas for young officers in all three present branches of the Armed Forces. The need for expert officer nose cone specialists, propulsion specialists, electronic guidance specialists, airframe (tank-age) experts, and ground-support specialists to supervise the enlisted men at the farflung missile sites could mount to a great national shortage in the 1960's unless preparatory steps are taken now.

Space Age Education—A Challenge

Space Age education in the United States and in the world? Only dynamic action will make this dream come true. The proper Space Age attitudes and social concepts will develop as teachers delve into the content and methodology of imparting "space" knowledge. These attitudes are essential if the citizens, present and future, are to meet the responsibilities of world leadership today and in the future.

The great challenge to Space Age education is to determine how soon it can provide a medium to help us keep abreast of the social changes which satellites have wrought, and to enlarge our thinking to a global and interplanetary basis.

There appears to be a paradox in much of present-day school curriculum, as to whether it is properly geared to the realities of the Space Age. This paradox is best summed up by the following true story.

The story has been going the rounds among the missile "bird-watchers" of Cape Canaveral, Florida, about two elementary school youngsters playing outside a nearby schoolyard during a recess period. As a giant rocket rose in the distance from behind the fenced-in Air Force Missile Test Center, one of the boys said to the other, "There goes an Atlas ICBM. Look, it's falling in flames."

His classmate pulled out his bubble gum and retorted, "Yeah, too bad; it should have gone over 5,000 miles."

The first boy then commented, "Do you know it stands over 80 feet tall, is 8½ feet wide and weighs over 90 tons?"

"Sure, and don't forget the thrust," said his playmate, "one hundred thousand pounds plus two boosters of 135,000 pounds each."

"Well, it's too bad they had to blow it up from the ground," the first one mused.

At this moment, the bell sounded, signifying the end of the recess. The second boy beckoned to his friend and remarked, "Heck, we better get back inside the school and string those doggone beads."

Our space world of tomorrow requires that we urgently prepare now for a comprehensive educational system so that our children will be able to enter the Space Age with no fears. This preparation includes education for other people's children as well as for our own.

As H. G. Wells once said, "Human history becomes more and more a race between education and disaster."

It is our responsibility to forestall the latter by keeping informed, and by fighting for better schools for our youth. If we can accomplish this end, then the true meaning and realization of spacepower will become manifest.

epilogue

a United Nations space program

I propose that we agree that outer space should be used only for peaceful purposes. We face a decisive moment in history in relation to this matter. Both the Soviet Union and the United States are now using outer space for the testing of missiles designed for military purposes. The time to stop is now.

President Dwight D. Eisenhower
In note to Premier Bulganin—January 12, 1958

ON January 15, 1958, the President of the UN General Assembly, Sir Leslie Munro of New Zealand, called for a meeting of world scientists and diplomats to lay the groundwork for the United Nations consideration of the "future of man in the spatial world." He said such a meeting would prepare the way for the 82-nation General Assembly to conduct a session in the fall of 1958 on "Space for Peace."

In order to ensure that outer space is used for peaceful purposes, we should begin thinking about a comprehensive UN-sponsored Space Program now!

Such a program should be monitored by a UN Space Agency. Its initial responsibility should be to develop a workable Space-power Timetable which would be flexible to advances and breakthroughs in the state-of-the-art of rocketry.

There is no reason to believe that the cost problem for an international Space Program cannot be worked out just as we have worked out similar programs for various global projects here on Earth. The heavier costs borne by the large and wealthier nations will be supplemented by the have-not nations, who will at least be able to render valuable ground support to the Space Program.

Anything short of a well-planned, unified Space Program could only lead to a repetition of the divisive exploitation of space and the planets patterned after our mistakes here on Earth. If space-power is to become a meaningful concept for those who have turned their eyes to contiguous space and beyond, then it means that those who believe in its potential to help ensure the peace of the world will have to act now and assume space leadership.

Senator Lyndon Johnson, the chairman of the Senate Pre-paredness subcommittee, in a significant radio speech on Janu-ary 14, 1958, assumed such leadership when he said that if the United States responds to the Space Age with its old pioneering spirit and gets forceful and bold leadership, it can "look beyond the danger evident now to see the horizons of peace in outer space."

He concluded with: "It would be appropriate and fitting for our nation to demonstrate its initiative before the United Na-tions by inviting all member nations to join in this adventure into outer space together. . . ."

acknowledgments

Grateful acknowledgment is made to the following publishers, authors, and other copyright holders for permission to reprint copyrighted material.

Every effort has been made to trace the source of all quoted material. If, inadvertently, copyrighted material has been included for which permission was not secured, the authors and the publisher extend their sincere apologies.

AMERICAN AVIATION PUBLICATIONS for an excerpt from the March, 1957, issue of *Missiles and Rockets*.

THE ANNALS OF THE AMERICAN ACADEMY OF POLITICAL AND SOCIAL SCIENCE for an excerpt from "The Geography of the Air" by Stefan T. Possony and Leslie Rosenzweig, from the May, 1955, issue of *The Annals of The American Academy of Political and Social Science*.

DR. FRANKLYN M. BRANLEY for an excerpt from *Toward Outer Space*. New York: Alumni Press.

JOHN COBB COOPER for an excerpt from his letter to *The London Times*, September 2, 1957.

DONALD K. DAVID for a statement made November 18, 1957.

SECRETARY OF STATE JOHN FOSTER DULLES for an excerpt from his address before the National Press Club, Washington, D.C., January 16, 1958.

BRIGADIER GENERAL HOLLINGSWORTH F. GREGORY for excerpts from statements made at the Astronautical Symposium, San Diego, California, February 18–20, 1957

ANDREW G. HALEY for excerpts from various statements.

HARPER & BROTHERS for an excerpt from *The Making of a Moon* by Arthur C. Clarke.

DR. C. WILFRED JENKS for excerpts from "International Law and Activities in Space" which is to be reprinted in *The Common Law of Mankind*. New York: Frederick A. Praeger, Inc. London: Stevens and Company.

LITTLE, BROWN & COMPANY for an excerpt from *Our Plundered Planet* by Fairfield Osborn.

JAMES T. MANGAN for excerpts from various statements.

DR. DONALD N. MICHAEL for an excerpt from the July, 1957, I.G.Y. *Newsletter*.

NEW YORK HERALD TRIBUNE for an excerpt from an article by Walter Lippmann.

THE NEW YORK TIMES for the editorial "The Shaggiest Dog," November 5, 1957; and an excerpt from the editorial "Man Into Space," December 5, 1957.

SATURDAY REVIEW for an excerpt from "Reflections on Sea and Space" by Peter Ritner, from the October 18, 1957, issue of *Saturday Review*.

DR. OSCAR SCHACHTER for an excerpt from a statement made in 1957.

MAJOR GENERAL BERNARD A. SCHRIEVER for excerpts from statements made in 1957.

SMITHSONIAN INSTITUTION for excerpts from "A Method of Reaching Extreme Altitudes" by Dr. Robert H. Goddard, from the *Smithsonian Miscellaneous Collections*, Vol. 71, No. 2, 1919.

TIME, INC. for an excerpt from "The Growing Air America" by Charles J. V. Murphy, from the June 18, 1956, issue of *Life*.

THE VIKING PRESS, INC. for an excerpt from V-2 by Dr. Walter Dornberger.

GENERAL THOMAS D. WHITE for excerpts from speeches made in 1956 and 1957.

The authors also wish to acknowledge the assistance and thoughtful encouragement of Major James F. Sunderman of the United States Air Force.

None of the material that appears in this book has been taken from classified sources.

index

A

ONE-HUNDRED-YEAR PROGRESS

UNMANNED FLIGHT SPECTRUM

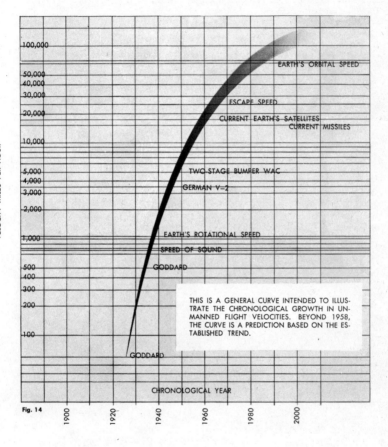

THIS IS A GENERAL CURVE INTENDED TO ILLUS-
TRATE THE CHRONOLOGICAL GROWTH IN UN-
MANNED FLIGHT VELOCITIES. BEYOND 1958,
THE CURVE IS A PREDICTION BASED ON THE ES-
TABLISHED TREND.

Fig. 14

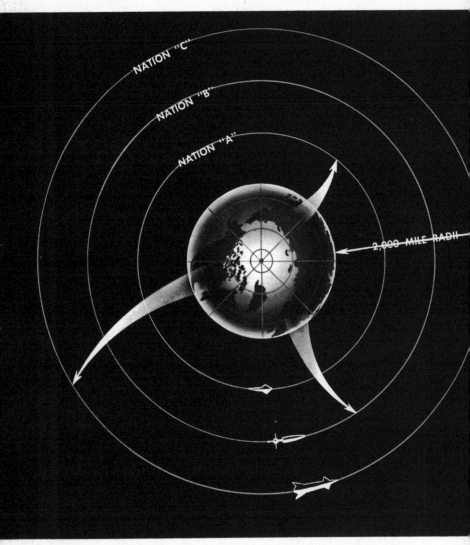

Fig. 15—Military space domination doctrine—theory of the further-most nationalistic penetration of space influencing control of the Earth through increased ability to dominate nations with lesser space-flight capabilities.

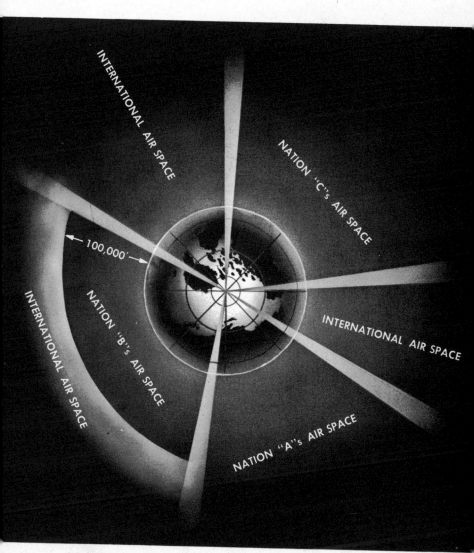

Fig. 16—A space supremacy doctrinal concept based on aircraft and missile control of national air space. Note: Nation B has no capability to control its air space over 100,000 feet. This theory is based on the present-day sovereign control of national air boundaries.

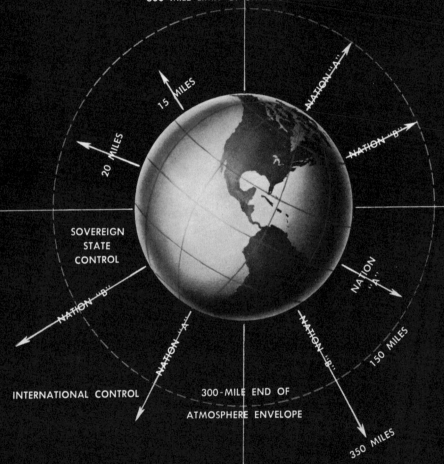

A
SCHACHTER'S AIR SPACE THEORY

STATE SOVEREIGNTY IS LIMITED TO THE HEIGHT AT WHICH AIRCRAFT AND BALLOONS CAN OPERATE.

B
JENKS' FREE SPACE THEORY

STATE SOVEREIGNTY IS LIMITED TO ACTIVITIES WITHIN THE LIMITS OF THE EARTH'S ATMOSPHERE ONLY.

FREE SPACE

300-MILE LIMIT OF STATE SOVEREIGNTY

15 MILES

20 MILES

NATION "A"

NATION "B"

SOVEREIGN
STATE
CONTROL

NATION "A"

NATION "B"

NATION "A"

NATION "B"

150 MILES

INTERNATIONAL CONTROL

300-MILE END OF

ATMOSPHERE ENVELOPE

350 MILES

FREE SPACE

Fig. 17

C
HALEY'S EXTRA-ATMOSPHERE MIGHT

EXTRA-ATMOSPHERE "MIGHT" BE SUBJECT TO SOVEREIGN CONTROL WITH INTERNATIONAL CONTROL FOR PEACEFUL PURPOSES.

D
COOPER'S CONTROL THEORY

SOVEREIGNTY EXTENDS AS FAR AS A NATION IS ABLE TO GOVERN THOSE EVENTS OCCURRING OVER ITS TERRITORY.

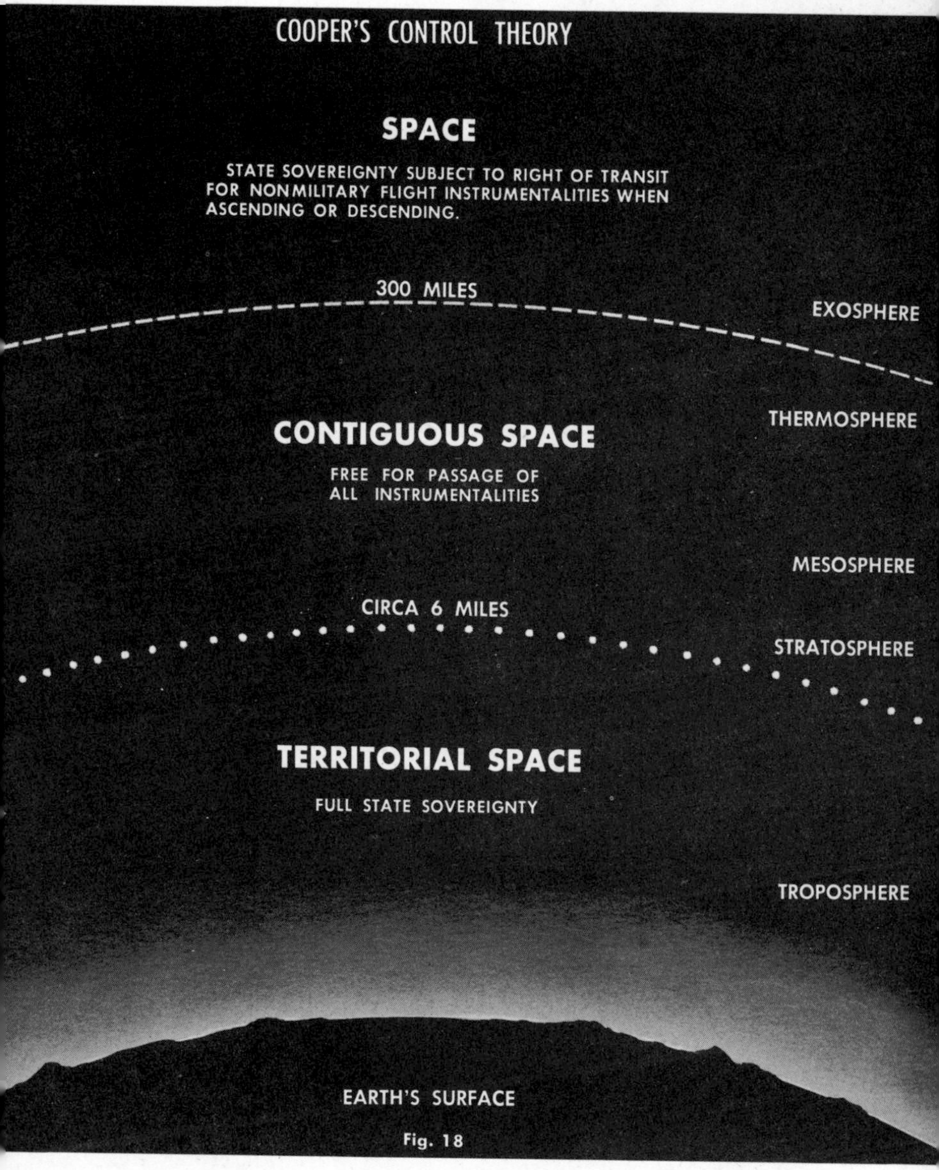

COOPER'S CONTROL THEORY

SPACE

STATE SOVEREIGNTY SUBJECT TO RIGHT OF TRANSIT
FOR NONMILITARY FLIGHT INSTRUMENTALITIES WHEN
ASCENDING OR DESCENDING.

300 MILES

EXOSPHERE

THERMOSPHERE

CONTIGUOUS SPACE

FREE FOR PASSAGE OF
ALL INSTRUMENTALITIES

MESOSPHERE

CIRCA 6 MILES

STRATOSPHERE

TERRITORIAL SPACE

FULL STATE SOVEREIGNTY

TROPOSPHERE

EARTH'S SURFACE

Fig. 18

Fig. 19—A central UN control and data processing center. This center has the responsibility of monitoring all flights between the Earth and the Moon. The lunar control center will have the responsibility of monitoring all future limited flights beyond the Moon.

O

P

Vulcan B2, British bomber, 32, 33

W

WAC Corporal, U.S. missile, 44
War, in space, 137
Warheads, nuclear, in missiles, 49, 50, 51, 53
Wasserfall, German World War II rockets, 38, 42
Water, as fluid for nuclear rocket, 115–116
Weather control, by space vehicles, 187
Weather forecasting, long-range, 90, 186–187
Weightlessness, in space flight, 185
Wells, H. G., 210
West Point, 205
Whipple, Fred, 16
White, Gen. Thomas D., 122, 207, 214
Wilson, Charles, 162
Wilson, Gil Robb, 121
Wire-guided missiles, French, 35, 36
Wizard Project of U. S. Air Force, 127
Wizard Island, Oregon, 104
Woomera Range, Australia, Anglo-Australian missile and rocket test facility, 31–32, 34
Wrap-around, solid propellant boost motors, 32, 33, 52
Wright, Orville, xv
Wright, Quincy, 170
WS-315 (Thor), U.S. missile, 51

X

X-rays, 192

Y

Youth, Space Age programs for, 198–200

Z

Zborowski, 35
Ziolkovsky, Konstantin E., 20
Zones, inspection, for missile control, 154; aerial-and-ground-inspection, 156
Zoomar-type television camera, 64
Zorin, Valerian A., 154, 157
Zuni, U. S. Navy missile, 46
Zwicky, Fritz, 70–71